AS Fast-Track

Chemistry

Lesley Owen

Series consultants **Geoff Black and Stuart Wall**

Page designer **Michelle Cannatella**

Cover designer **Kube Ltd**

Pearson Education Limited
Edinburgh Gate
Harlow
Essex CM20 2JE, England
and Associated Companies throughout the world

ISBN 0 582 43235-9

British Library Cataloguing-in-Publication Data

A catalogue record for this book is available from the British Library.

Set by 3 in Optima and Tekton
Printed by Ashford Colour Press, Gosport, Hants

Contents

Read this first!

TWO WAYS TO USE THIS BOOK...

This book is designed to be used:

Either

- On its own – work through all the exercises for a quick run-through of your subject. This will take you about 24 hours altogether.

or

- As part of the *Revision Express* system:

1 Read through the topic in the *Revision Express A-level Study Guide* (or similar book).

2 Work through the exercises in this book.

3 Go to www.revision-express.com for extra exam questions and model answers.

4 For even more depth and detail, refer back to your textbook or class notes, and visit the web links from www.revision-express.com.

HOW THE BOOK WORKS

The book is divided into two-page revision sessions. To make your revision really effective, study one session at a time.

Have a short break between sessions – that way you'll learn more!

Each session has two parts:

1st page: the first page on each topic contains interactive exercises to nail down the basics. Follow the instructions in the margin and write your answers in the spaces provided.

2nd page: the second page contains exam questions. Sometimes you'll answer the exam question directly, but more often you'll use it as a starting point for in-depth revision exercises. In each case, follow the extra instructions in the margin.

REMEMBER: the answers in the back are for the revision exercises – they are not necessarily model answers to the exam questions themselves. For model answers to a selection of exam questions go to www.revision-express.com.

All the pages are hole-punched, so you can remove them and put them in your folder.

TRACK YOUR PROGRESS

The circles beside each topic heading let you track your progress.

If a topic is hard, fill in one circle. If it's easy, fill in all three. If you've only filled in one or two circles go back to the topic later.

TOPIC HEADING ●●○

EXAM BOARDS

You might not need to work through every session in this book. Check that your exam board is listed above the topic heading before you start a session.

AS AQA EDEXCEL OCR WJEC

This book covers the most popular topics. For full information about your syllabus, contact the relevant exam board or go to their website.

AQA
(Assessment and Qualifications Alliance)
Publications department, Stag Hill House,
Guildford, Surrey GU2 5XJ – www.aqa.org.uk

EDEXCEL
Stuart House, 32 Russell Square, London
WC1B 5DN – www.edexcel.org.uk

OCR
(Oxford, Cambridge and Royal Society of Arts)
1 Hills Road, Cambridge CB2 1GG –
www.ocr.org.uk

DON'T FORGET

Exam questions have been specially written for this book. Ask your teacher or the exam board for the official sample papers to add to the questions given here.

COMMENTS PLEASE!

However you use this book, we'd welcome your comments. Just go to www.revision-express.com and tell us what you think!

GOOD LUCK!

Atoms and atomic mass

Atoms and atomic mass

Atoms are unbelievably small and have equally small masses. Since these small numbers are hard to work with, a relative scale of masses is used, where everything is compared to the mass of an atom of carbon-12, which is assigned a mass of 12.

Some definitions

Define each of these terms. The first one has been done for you.

THE JARGON
A weighted average takes into account that isotopes are not present in equal amounts.

A_r, relative atomic mass — Weighted average mass of an atom compared to one-twelfth the mass of a ^{12}C atom

M_r, relative molecular mass
Sum of all the RAM of the atoms in the element shown in the formula compared 1/12th mass of carbon-12 atom.

Isotopic mass
The mass of a particular isotope compared to 1/12th . . . .

Formula mass
Average mass of formula unit compared . . . .

Basics of mass spectroscopy

Relative masses are measured using a mass spectrometer. These five statements outline its principles.

Number the boxes to show the order in which the stages occur.

- [3] The positive ions are accelerated using a high voltage and deflected by a magnetic field
- [2] An outer electron is knocked off the atom or molecule using an electron gun. Positive ions are formed
- [4] Ions of low mass are deflected more than heavier ions
- [1] The substance is turned to a gas and bombarded with electrons
- [5] Ions are detected and a mass spectrum is produced

Calculating relative atomic mass from isotopic data

If a sample of an element is examined, there will be different peaks in the spectrum due to the different isotopes it contains. If a sample of lithium is examined, two peaks are seen. The heights of the peaks can be measured to find the percentage of each isotope present.

Here is some data for lithium: 7.42% is ^{6}Li and 92.58% is ^{7}Li.

Use the data provided to calculate the relative atomic mass of lithium.

$$\frac{(7.42 \times 6) + (92.58 \times 7)}{100} = 6.93$$

Turn the page for some exam questions on this topic ➤

Exam question 1

Here is a simplified mass spectrum for lead. The height of each peak is proportional to the percentage of that isotope present. Using this spectrum, calculate the relative atomic mass of lead.

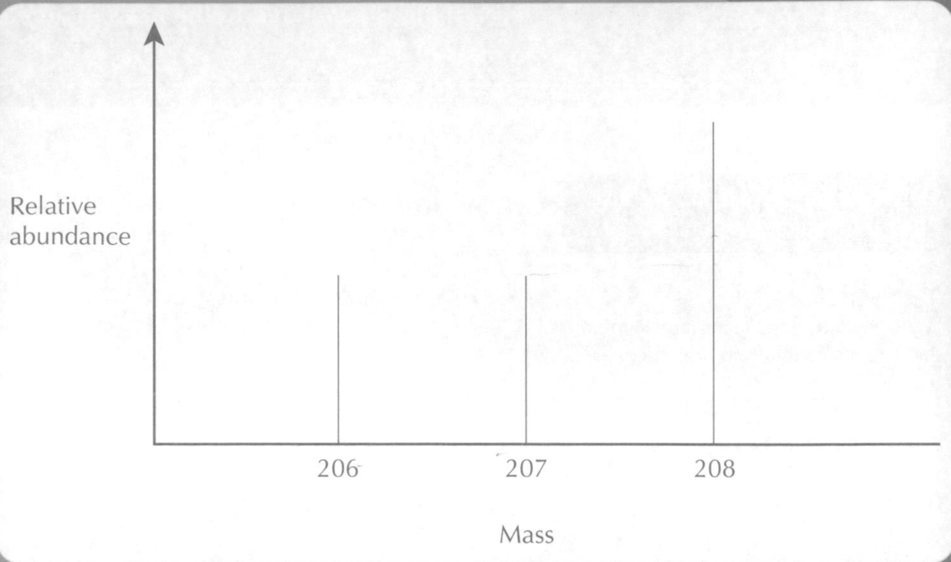

How many isotopes are present?

3

Measure the relative peak heights and add them together. What value do you get?

What fraction of each isotope is present?

Find the weighted average of the isotopes.

Exam question 2

Give two uses of mass spectroscopy.

Exam question 3

The mass spectrum of chlorine, Cl_2, has peaks at 35, 37 and 70. Interpret these peaks and predict which other two peaks should also be present.

SYLLABUS CHECK

Only WJEC will require you to interpret data for simple organic molecules.

DON'T FORGET

The covalent bond may be broken during ionization. Show the charge on the ion.

Calculations in chemistry

Calculations can involve reacting masses, volumes of gases or concentrations of solutions. They involve the idea of a mole.

WHAT IS A MOLE?

Explain what you understand by a mole. In your definition you should refer to isotope carbon-12 and Avogadro's number.

is the amount of substance that contains 6.02×10^{23} atoms, ions or molecules compared $\frac{1}{12}$th mass of Carbon-12 atom.

Work out the molar mass (mass of 1 mole) for the substances given in the table. Show your working.

Cl_2

CaO

$MgCl_2$

$Fe(OH)_2$

H_2SO_4

DON'T FORGET
To find the number of moles, you divide the mass (in grams) by the mass of 1 mole, $n = m / M_r$.

When gases are involved, what do you need to remember?

Draw lines to link a statement in the first column with one in the second.

1 1 m^3 =	m^3
2 1 mole of any gas at RTP occupies	1 000 000 cm^3
3 In $pV = nRT$, V must be given in	24 dm^3
4 1 mole of any gas at STP occupies	Pa
5 In $pV = nRT$, p must be given in	1000 cm^3
6 1 dm^3 =	22.4 dm^3

SYLLABUS CHECK
The formula $pV = nRT$ is only in the AQA and WJEC syllabuses.

For solutions

When solutions are involved, you need to use the formula $n = cv$. In this equation, what do the symbols represent and what are their units?

Symbol	Quantity	Unit
n		
c		
v		

Some terminology

What do you understand by the terms 'empirical formula' and 'molecular formula'?

Empirical formula

Molecular formula

Turn the page for some exam questions on this topic ➤

Exam question 1

When 4.86 g of magnesium undergo complete combustion in oxygen they form 8.06 g of oxide. Calculate the empirical formula of the oxide and then find the volume of oxygen reacted at RTP.

DON'T FORGET

When doing calculations, find the number of moles, then find the ratios, then work out the answer.

Write a balanced equation for the combustion of magnesium. Include state symbols.

Calculate the volume of oxygen that is reacted (at RTP).

The magnesium oxide then reacts with 0.50 mol dm^{-3} HCl. What volume of this acid will be needed to make it react completely?

Write an equation for the reaction of MgO with HCl.

Find moles.

Refer to the equation for ratios.

Find the answer.

Atomic structure

Atoms are the building blocks of chemistry and you need to know about the structure of an atom.

STRUCTURE OF THE ATOM

Here are the properties of the three subatomic particles.

Complete this table to show their properties.

	Relative charge	Relative mass	Where found
protons	+1		
neutrons			
electrons		1/1 840	orbiting

Each different element is represented by a symbol. For example, the symbol for potassium is K and it may be shown like this:

mass number 39
atomic number 19 $^{39}_{19}K$

What does the proton number tell us?

What does the mass number tell us?

Complete this chart to show how many protons, neutrons and electrons there are in each atom or ion. $^{39}_{19}K$ and $^{40}_{19}K$ are isotopes.

Atom / ion	Protons	Neutrons	Electrons
$^{39}_{19}K$			
$^{40}_{19}K$			
$^{39}_{19}K^{+}$			

Explain what an isotope is.

DON'T FORGET

You should be able to show the electron arrangement of the atoms up to $Z = 36$ using spdf notation.

Show the electron arrangement for K.

Define, using equations, what is meant by first and second ionization energies. Ionization energy is the energy required to remove one mole of electrons.

Turn the page for some exam questions on this topic ➤

For more on this topic, see pages 12–13 of the *Revision Express A-level Study Guide*

EXAM QUESTION 1

Give the spdf notation for Se, which has a proton number of 34.

Give the spdf notation for Mn^{2+}, which has a proton number of 25.

DON'T FORGET
Transition metals always lose their outer s electrons before they lose their d electrons.

Draw a diagram to show the electronic configuration of oxygen, atomic number 8, using an 'electrons in boxes' notation.

Complete the energy level diagram for Al to show how electrons fill the energy levels.

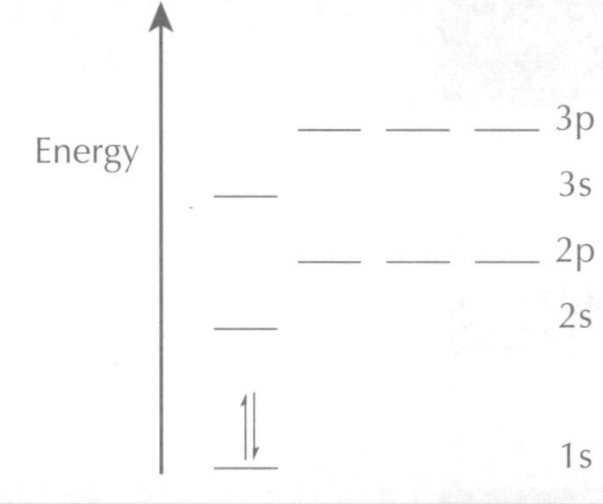

DON'T FORGET
The order of filling orbitals is shown on this diagram.

EXAM QUESTION 2

LINKS
For a more detailed discussion of trends in ionization energy, see pp. 37–38.

The successive ionization energies of an element vary like this.
To which group of the periodic table does the element belong? Explain your reasoning.

Look for a big jump from row to row.

Number of the ionization energy	Ionization energy (kJ mol^{-1})
1	1 060
2	1 900
3	2 920
4	4 960
5	6 280
6	21 200
7	25 900
8	30 500

DON'T FORGET
The factors that affect ionization energy are nuclear charge, electron shielding and the distance of the outer electron from the nucleus.

Ionic bonding

Ionic bonding is the electrostatic attraction between two oppositely charged ions and occurs when atoms with large differences in electronegativity combine.

THE JARGON
Electronegativity is the ability of an atom to attract the bonding electrons towards it.

When does ionic bonding occur?

Here are some statements about electronegativity.

Tick the statements that are true.

- It increases as you go across periods ☐
- It increases as you go down groups ☐
- A metal and a non-metal will generally have a large difference in electronegativity ☐

Draw a ring round the compounds from this list that you would expect to be ionic.

Li_2O CH_4 CO_2 $NaCl$ NH_3 MgO H_2O

The electron arrangement of Li is $1s^2 2s^1$ and that of oxygen is $1s^2 2s^2 2p^4$. What does each of these atoms need to do in order to have a full outer shell of electrons like their nearest noble gases?

What will these oppositely charged ions do?

Drawing diagrams of ionic bonding

This loss and gain of electrons can be shown using dot and cross diagrams. For simplicity, only the outer shell electrons are shown.

Here is such a diagram for Li_2O.

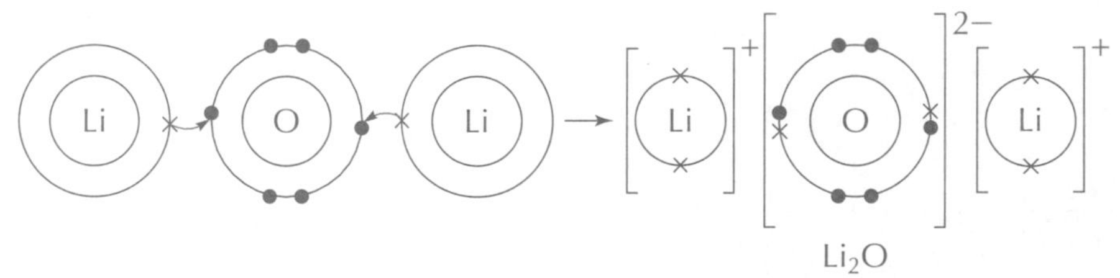

Draw dot and cross diagrams for MgO and label the ions that form.

What sort of structure do the oppositely charged ions form?

THE JARGON
A lattice is some sort of regular and ordered arrangement of particles held together by some sort of force.

Turn the page for some exam questions on this topic ➤

DON'T FORGET
When asked to show bonding, always check whether you should draw a diagram for ionic or covalent bonding. In this case there is clearly a metal and a non-metal.

EXAM QUESTION 1

(a) Draw a dot and cross diagram to show how the bonding in sodium chloride occurs.

DON'T FORGET
If you think ionic, then think giant ionic lattice.

WATCH OUT
When you draw the structure, take care to avoid using solid lines between the ions as these are used to represent covalent bonds.

(b) Draw a diagram to show a sodium chloride lattice.

(c) Describe what properties you would expect sodium chloride to have; relate these properties to its structure.

Ask yourself how easy it will be to break down the structure and what will happen when it does break down.

LINKS
To find out why water is such a good solvent, see pp. 17–18.

(d) How would you expect the melting point of magnesium oxide to compare with that of sodium chloride?

It is the attraction of the ions that determines the melting point. Think about the ionic attractions in MgO and NaCl.

Covalent bonding

When the difference in electronegativity between two atoms is small (generally between two non-metals), the atoms must share their electrons in order to gain full outer shells. These atoms bond covalently.

What is a covalent bond?

When a pair of electrons is shared between atoms, there is a force of attraction between the nuclei of each atom and the shared pair of electrons. This is a covalent bond. A single bond is shown as a single 'stick' joining the two atoms, e.g. H–Br.

How do we draw covalent bonds?

The sharing of electrons can be shown using dot and cross diagrams.

Draw dot and cross diagrams and stick diagrams for the following molecules: H_2, HCl, H_2O, CO_2. The first one has been done for you.

H–H

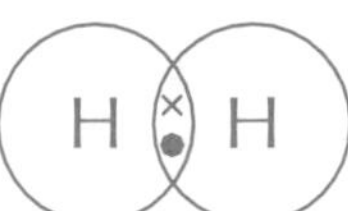

DON'T FORGET
It is easiest to show the outer electrons only. You can use circles to show the inner shells but there's no need.

THE JARGON
The pairs of electrons not involved in bonding are called lone pairs.

Dative covalent bonds (coordinate bonds)

These occur when both electrons of the covalent bond originate from one of the atoms. They behave just like covalent bonds and they are shown as an arrow in stick diagrams.

Draw a dot and cross diagram to show the covalent bonding in $AlCl_3$. Note that Al only has six electrons around it, not eight. In order to obtain electrons in its outside shell, $AlCl_3$ dimerizes. Draw a stick diagram to show how this dimer forms.

DON'T FORGET
You will need arrows.

A sliding scale between ionic and covalent

Ionic bonding occurs when electronegativity differences are large and covalent bonding occurs when they are small. In between there is a sliding scale, and if the difference is moderate then we may get an ionic substance with a degree of covalent character.

Rewrite this list in order of increasing ionic character.

CsF CH_4 F_2 HF $AlCl_3$ NaCl

increasing ionic character →

LINKS
To remind yourself about electronegativity, see p. 11.

Turn the page for some exam questions on this topic ➤

EXAM QUESTION 1

Would you expect the following compounds to be covalent or ionic?

potassium sulphide

hydrogen sulphide

sodium hydride

carbon dioxide

EXAM QUESTION 2

Hints are given below but try to do the question without them first.

(a) Draw both dot and cross diagrams and stick diagrams to show the bonding in C_2H_4 (ethene) and NH_3 (ammonia).

DON'T FORGET
Ethene contains a double bond. Ammonia has a lone pair.

(b) Draw both dot and cross diagrams and stick diagrams to show the bonding in an ammonium ion.

DON'T FORGET
You must show all the outer electrons, not just the bonding electrons. You will need to draw an arrow on the stick diagram.

(c) Draw a diagram to show how the iodine molecules are arranged in a crystal of iodine.

SYLLABUS CHECK
Only AQA and WJEC need a drawing to show the structure of iodine.

(d) Explain why the members of group 7, the halogens, are all volatile and why the boiling temperature increases down the group.

WATCH OUT
Never just say that the halogens are volatile because they are covalently bonded. Covalent bonds are strong. What is it that holds one molecule to another?

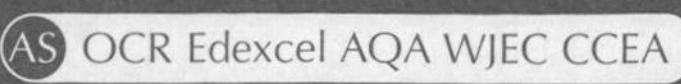

Shapes of molecules and ions

When atoms combine to form molecules, we can work out the shape by using the electron pair repulsion theory.

Rules for working out the shape of molecules

Complete the last two columns of this table to remind yourself about the shapes of molecules. Show the bond angle on your diagrams.

SYLLABUS CHECK
Only Edexcel and AQA include negative ions.

Pairs of electrons	Based on the shape	Lone pairs	Shape	Diagram
2	linear	0		
3	trigonal	0		
3	trigonal	1		
4	tetrahedral	0		
4	tetrahedral	1		
4	tetrahedral	2		
6	octahedral	0		
6	octahedral	2		

Try this out for a water molecule

The bond angle in water is about 105°. Why is it less than 109°, the tetrahedral angle?

Turn the page for some exam questions on this topic ➤

EXAM QUESTION 1

Draw a dot and cross diagram for each molecule. Then draw a stick model for each and work out the angles

DON'T FORGET

Draw a dot and cross diagram for the molecule. Count the number of electron pairs around the central atom. Count the number of lone pairs.

SYLLABUS CHECK

Edexcel and AQA require a little bit more than the other boards. Make sure that you can also draw the SO_4^{2-}, NO_3^-, CO_3^{2-} ions and the bipyramidal PCl_5 molecule.

For each of the molecules or ions below, draw a diagram to show the shape and indicate all of the bond angles.

CH_4

CO_2

NH_4^+

$BeCl_2$

SF_6

EXAM QUESTION 2

First draw dot and cross diagrams.

Now draw stick diagrams that show the shape.

Label each atom to show the polarity of each bond. Use δ+ or δ− to show this. Remember electronegativity increases across the period.

The molecule is non-polar if the individual dipoles cancel out but polar if they do not. The shape helps you decide.

Use diagrams to help you explain why BF_3 is a non-polar molecule whereas NH_3 is said to be polar.

Intermolecular forces

These are the forces that hold discrete, covalently bonded molecules together and which determine properties such as melting and boiling temperatures and solubility in water. They are van der Waals forces, permanent dipoles and hydrogen bonding.

Bond polarity and permanent dipoles

The existence of permanent dipoles in a molecule means that molecules are attracted to one another, and this means melting and boiling temperatures are higher than you might otherwise predict.

For each of these molecules, draw the shape of the molecule, mark on any polar bonds and label the molecule as polar or non-polar

Cl_2		
HCl		
CCl_4		

THE JARGON
Molecules that are polar are said to have a permanent dipole.

Van der Waals forces

Even if molecules are not polar, they will still have van der Waals forces attracting them together; van der Waals forces are temporary dipoles.

Explain what you understand by the term 'temporary dipole'.

SPEED LEARNING
Hydrogen bonding can only occur when hydrogen is directly attached to **n**itrogen, **o**xygen or **f**luorine. Remember **NOF**.

Hydrogen bonding

This is an especially strong attraction that occurs between a polar hydrogen on one molecule and a lone pair of electrons present on a very electronegative atom of another molecule.

Draw a diagram to show how hydrogen bonding occurs between two water molecules.

Turn the page for some exam questions on this topic ➤

For more on this topic, see pages 16–21 of the *Revision Express A-level Study Guide*

Exam question 1

Explain the following statements.

(a) The noble gases all have low boiling temperatures but the boiling temperature increases as you go down the group

DON'T FORGET
To explain the physical properties of a substance you need to work out what types of bonding and structure are present.

(b) Water is a liquid

DON'T FORGET
There's a particularly strong intermolecular force that could account for this. See if you can remember it.

SYLLABUS CHECK
Edexcel also needs you to be able to draw a diagram of ice.

(c) Ice floats on water

DON'T FORGET
Ask yourself why one substance floats in another substance. Try to explain what could cause this.

(d) Methane is a gas

DON'T FORGET
Methane is CH_4.

(e) Ethanol (CH_3CH_2OH) will mix well with water, but its isomer methoxymethane (CH_3OCH_3) will not

THE JARGON
Isomers have the same molecular formula but different structures.

DON'T FORGET
CH_3OCH_3 is a gas at room temperature.

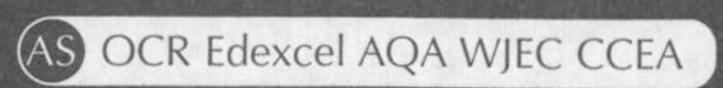

Giant structures

Why is diamond so hard if the bonding in carbon is covalent? Why do metals conduct? Why is it that only some substances dissolve in water?

DIAMOND AND GRAPHITE

In these two forms of carbon, the carbon atoms are held together by covalent bonds in a giant lattice.

Label these diagrams to show which is the diamond structure and which is the graphite structure.

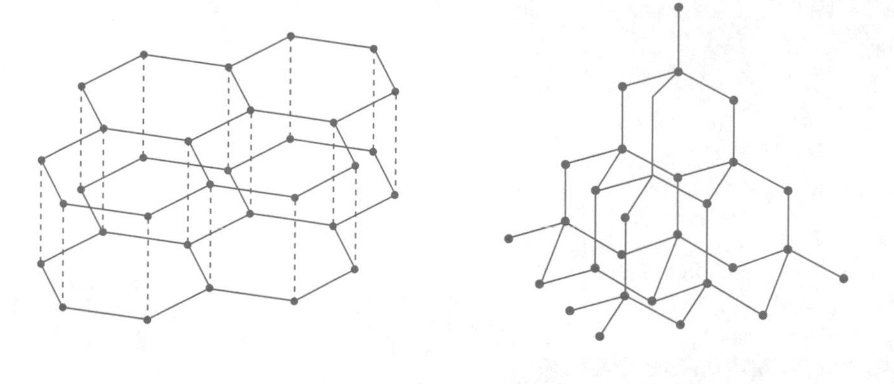

Tick the statements about diamond and graphite that are correct.

Diamond conducts electricity because it is a giant lattice	☐
Graphite conducts electricity because one of the electrons on each carbon is delocalized between layers	☐
There is strong bonding within a layer of graphite but there are only weak attractions between layers	☐
The bonds in diamond are easily broken because they are covalent	☐
Diamond cannot conduct because all of the electrons are localized in bonds	☐

SYLLABUS CHECK

For CCEA you need to know that quartz also consists of a giant lattice, with Si and O covalently bonded.

METALLIC BONDING

Use these words to construct a statement that describes metallic bonding: mobile, lattice, bonding, electrons, ions, giant, attraction, sea, metallic, electrostatic.

RELATING STRUCTURE AND BONDING TO PROPERTIES

Place a T beside a statement if it is true and a tick beside the explanation if it is correct.

Statement		Explanation	
Ionic compounds have high melting temperatures		A strong attraction between oppositely charged ions	
Metals conduct electricity		Their ions are free to move	
Simple molecular compounds have low melting temperatures		This is because they are covalently bonded	
Ionic compounds conduct electricity when molten		Their ions are free to move when molten	
Boiling temperature of noble gases increases as you go down the group		Increasing strength of van der Waals forces as number of electrons increases	

Turn the page for some exam questions on this topic ➤

EXAM QUESTION 1

Describe the bonding and structure in sodium chloride, diamond and iodine. Draw diagrams to show each structure. Describe and explain their physical properties.

First work out what type of bonding will be in each and what type of structure it has. Next draw a diagram of each structure.

	Sodium chloride	Diamond	Iodine
Bonding			
Structure			
Diagram		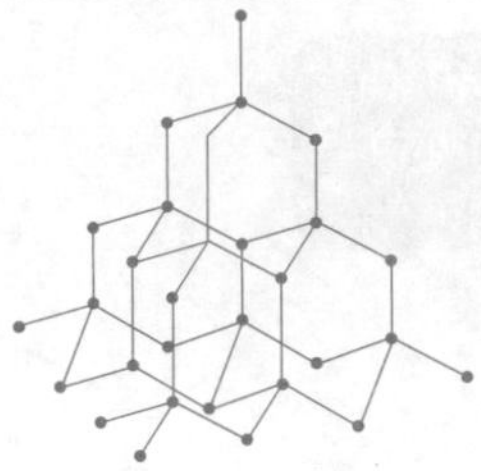	

SYLLABUS CHECK
OCR and Edexcel do not require knowledge of iodine's structure. Check your own syllabus to see if it specifies other structures you should know.

Then I would start to describe and explain the properties of each. Do this for each in turn. List the key points and reasoning.

Your final answer could be given in a table like this. It certainly helps to keep you focused.

SYLLABUS CHECK
Edexcel does not require details of solubility.

Properties of sodium chloride	Explanation of properties

Properties of diamond	Explanation of properties

SYLLABUS CHECK
OCR and Edexcel do not require knowledge of iodine's structure or properties.

Properties of iodine	Explanation of properties

Starting energetics

Energy may be taken in during a reaction (endothermic) or energy may be given out during a reaction (exothermic). The study of these energy changes is known as energetics. These changes are called *enthalpy* changes.

Enthalpy profile diagrams

These changes are often shown on enthalpy profile diagrams.

Label one of these diagrams as endothermic and the other as exothermic. Label the activation energy on both.

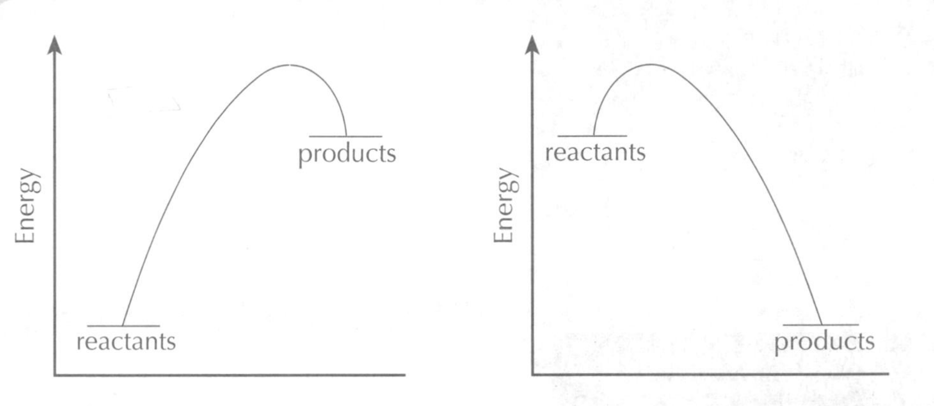

THE JARGON
The activation energy is the minimum energy that colliding particles must have in order for a reaction to occur.

For each reaction given, tick the correct column to say whether the reaction is endothermic or exothermic.

	Endothermic	Exothermic
Methane burning		✓
Respiration		✓
Decomposing calcium carbonate	✓	
Photosynthesis	✓	
Magnesium reacting with acid		✓

Bond breaking and making

Bond breaking is always **endothermic.**
Bond making is always **exothermic.**

Highlight the key points in this statement.

A measure of the amount of energy stored in a chemical system is the enthalpy (H) and enthalpy changes (ΔH) that can be measured when reactions occur. In an exothermic reaction, energy is given out; it is lost to the surroundings and ΔH is negative (−ve).

Define what is meant by these terms.

Enthalpy change of formation, ΔH_f

is the ΔH when 1 mol of compound is formed from it's element in the st states under standard conditions.

Standard conditions

25°C/298°C – temp
con – 1mol dm⁻³
atm P – 1.01 Nm⁻²

Enthalpy of combustion, ΔH_c

ΔH when 1 mol of substances is completely burning in O2 under st cond.

THE JARGON
Average bond enthalpy is the average energy needed to break one mole of a specified type of covalent bonds.

Turn the page for some exam questions on this topic ➤

For more on this topic, see pages 30–35 of the *Revision Express A-level Study Guide*

Exam question 1

Use the bond enthalpies below to calculate the enthalpy of combustion of methane.

First you must write a balanced equation using displayed formulae.

THE JARGON
A displayed formula shows the placing of bonds and the type of bond between each atom.

WATCH OUT
Bond enthalpies always have positive ΔH values since, by definition, bonds are broken.

Bond	Average bond enthalpy (kJ mol^{-1})
C−C	+347
C−H	+413
C=O	+805
H−O	+464
O=O	+498

Now write down two headings side by side, one for bonds broken and one for bonds made. Work out how many of each type of bond are broken and made.

Find the total energy taken in as bonds are broken, and the total energy given out as bonds form.

Add these totals together to get the overall enthalpy change.

Think of the values you are using.

A data book gives the enthalpy of combustion as −890 kJ mol^{-1}. Can you explain why the value you have calculated above is different (and less correct)?

DON'T FORGET
It is the high strength of the C=O bond that is largely responsible for the overall change in enthalpy being negative (exothermic).

Draw an enthalpy profile for this reaction.

Calculating enthalpy changes

You will have carried out experiments to measure some enthalpy changes and will have used Hess's law in calculations.

Measuring enthalpy of combustion, ΔH_c, by experiment

This will involve burning a fuel, heating some water and measuring its temperature rise.

List the measurements you need to make.

You will also need to know the specific heat capacity of the water.

You will need to use the equation: $Q = mc\,\Delta T$. For each quantity in this equation, say what it is and give its units.

Symbol	Quantity	Units
Q		
m		
c		
ΔT		

Try this question. Hide the hints if you don't need them.

100.0 g water at 20 °C were heated to 100 °C using a spirit burner containing ethanol. The mass of ethanol used was 1.20 g. Calculate the enthalpy of combustion for ethanol. Use $c = 4.18\ \text{J g}^{-1}\,°\text{C}^{-1}$.

Calculate the energy given to the water.

Find the number of moles of ethanol burnt.

Find the energy given to the water per mole of ethanol burnt.

What is ΔH_c for ethanol?

Hess's law

THE JARGON

Hess's law states that the overall energy change does not depend on the route taken, but only on the initial and final conditions.

This is used to find enthalpy changes that cannot be measured directly.

$$\tfrac{1}{2}O_{2\,(g)} + C_{(s)} + \tfrac{1}{2}O_{2\,(g)} \xrightarrow{\Delta H_1} CO_{(g)} + \tfrac{1}{2}O_{2\,(g)}$$

ΔH_2 (from $\tfrac{1}{2}O_{2\,(g)} + C_{(s)} + \tfrac{1}{2}O_{2\,(g)}$ to $CO_{2\,(g)}$); ΔH_3 (from $CO_{(g)} + \tfrac{1}{2}O_{2\,(g)}$ to $CO_{2\,(g)}$)

What are ΔH_1, ΔH_2, ΔH_3 in this Hess cycle?

ΔH_1 is

ΔH_2 is

ΔH_3 is

Write an equation in terms of ΔH_2 and ΔH_3 that would allow you to calculate ΔH_1.

$\Delta H_1 =$

Turn the page for some exam questions on this topic ➤

Exam question 1

Write an equation for the value you are trying to find. Then draw an energy cycle beneath it.

Use the following values of ΔH to find a value for the enthalpy change of formation of propane (C_3H_8).

Substance	Enthalpy change (kJ mol^{-1})
$C_3H_{8\,(g)}$	$\Delta H_c = -2\,219$
$CO_{2\,(g)}$	$\Delta H_f = -393$
$H_2O_{\,(l)}$	$\Delta H_f = -286$

Add oxygen to both sides and draw arrows to form the products of burning. Check the directions of the arrows match the ΔH values you are given.

Write the enthalpy changes onto the arrows. Remember to take the number of moles into account.

Write an equation for finding ΔH_f for propane. Reverse the sign for values where you have to go the wrong way along the arrow.

Exam question 2

Using the following ΔH_f values, calculate an enthalpy change for the reaction of Br_2 with ethene, shown in the equation below. What does this value tell you about the stability of bromoethane compared to bromine and ethene?

$Br_{2(g)} + C_2H_{4(g)} \rightarrow C_2H_4Br_{2(g)}$

Substance	ΔH_f (kJ mol^{-1})
$Br_{2(g)}$	+31
$C_2H_{4(g)}$	+52
$C_2H_4Br_{2(g)}$	−38

WATCH OUT

Br_2 does not have ΔH_f of zero as expected for elements. This is because it is not in its standard state in this equation.

First draw a suitable Hess cycle.

Now write an expression for ΔH_r and substitute the values.

What does a negative value for an enthalpy of reaction tell you?

Rates of reaction

The study of how fast a reaction proceeds is sometimes called kinetics. You need to know the factors that affect the rate of a reaction and why they do so.

COLLISION THEORY

LINKS
For a reminder of how activation energy is defined, see p. 21.

For a successful reaction to occur, particles must collide and they must collide with enough energy to break existing bonds; in other words, they must overcome the activation energy.

FACTORS THAT AFFECT THE RATE OF A REACTION

Link the change in the first column with the effect in the second by joining the *.

Increase temperature	*	*	Molecules collide more often
Increase gas pressure	*	*	Particles collide more often and with more energy
Increase solution concentration	*	*	Particles collide more often
Add a catalyst	*	*	Larger surface over which reaction can occur
Increase surface area of solid reactants	*	*	Lowers the activation energy

THE MAXWELL–BOLTZMANN DISTRIBUTION

This shows the range of energies that molecules of a gas may have at a given temperature, T_1. The area under the curve shows the total number of particles present. On the energy axis, E_a represents the activation energy.

On this graph, shade in the area which shows those molecules that have sufficient energy to react successfully at temperature T_1.

Draw another curve to show the distribution at a higher temperature, T_2, and using a different colour, shade in the proportion of molecules that can now overcome the activation barrier.

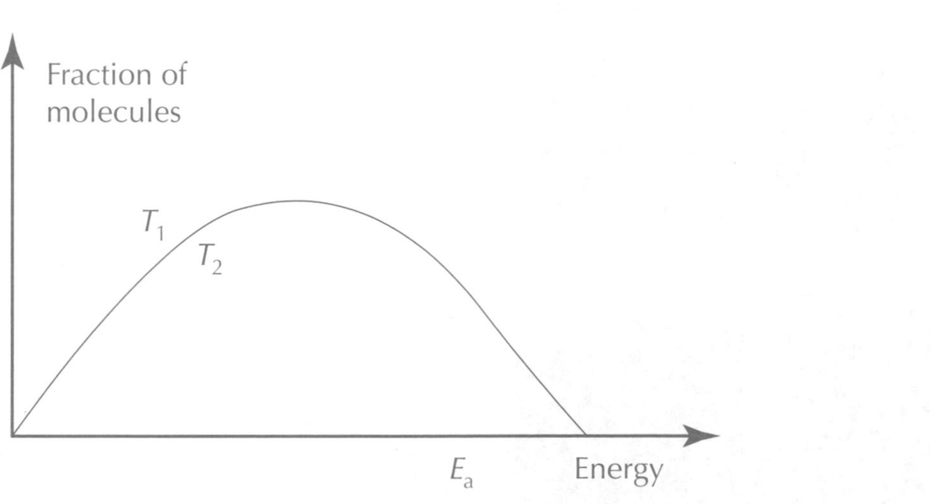

Use your graph to explain why small increases in temperature can lead to large increases in rate of reaction.

Turn the page for some exam questions on this topic ➤

EXAM QUESTION 1

An excess of zinc granules and 100 cm^3 of 0.1 mol dm^{-3} hydrochloric acid were reacted. The volume of hydrogen formed was measured at 1 minute intervals and here are the results.

Time (min)	Volume H_2 (cm^3)	Time (min)	Volume H_2 (cm^3)
0	0	6	102
1	20	7	111
2	42	8	118
3	62	9	120
4	79	10	120
5	90		

You should always plot the independent variable (the one you control) on the *x*-axis and the dependent variable (the one you are measuring) on the *y*-axis.

(a) Plot a graph of these results.

(b) Sketch onto your graph the following labelled curves for experiments carried out at the same temperature.

P 100 cm^3 of 0.1 mol dm^{-3} HCl, excess powdered Zn

Q 50 cm^3 of 0.1 mol dm^{-3} HCl, excess powdered Zn

R 100 cm^3 of 0.1 mol dm^{-3} HCl, excess powdered Zn with a $CuSO_4$ catalyst

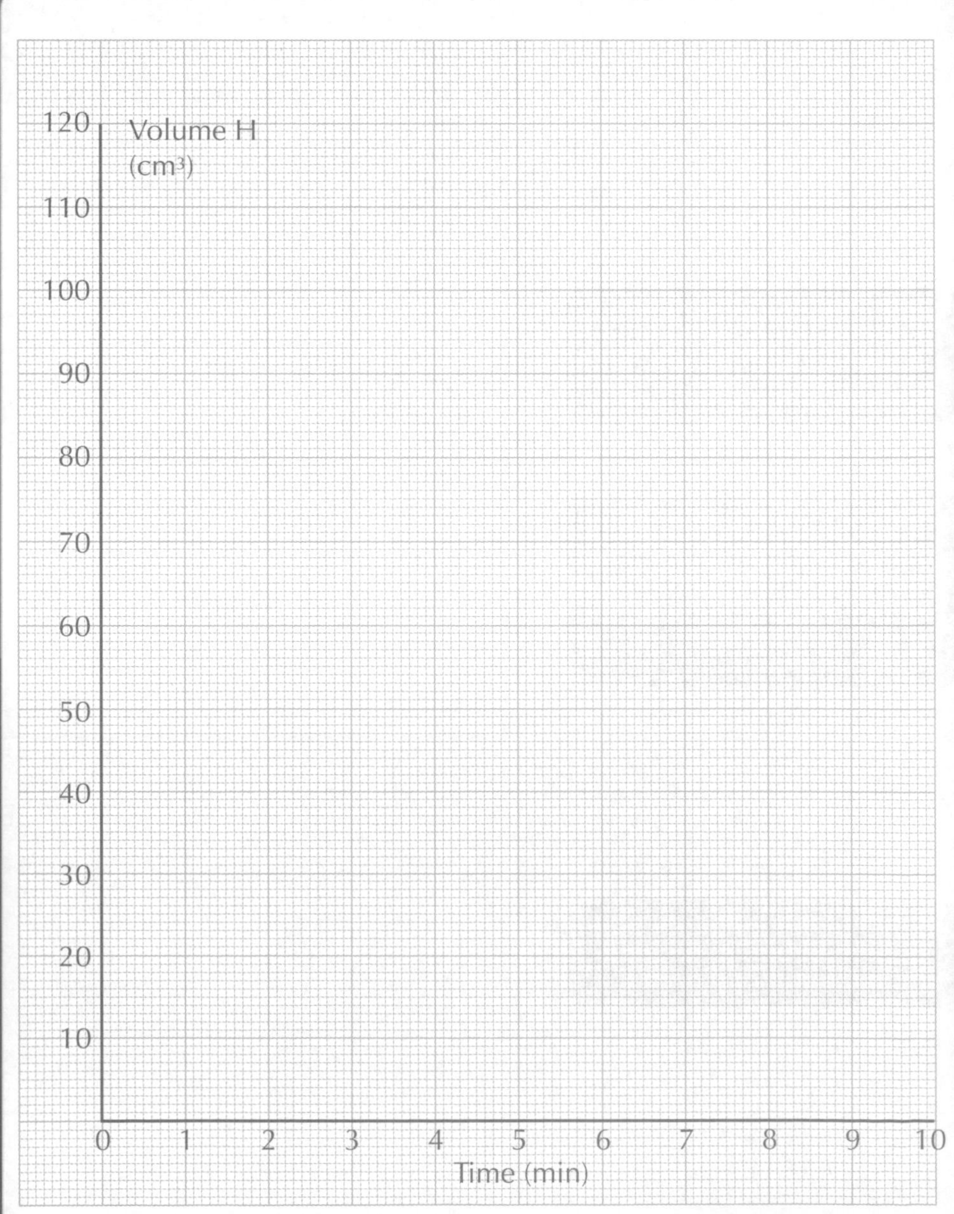

Using catalysts

Catalysts are substances that alter the rate of a reaction without being used up themselves. They have considerable economic importance.

How does a catalyst work?

Catalysts provide an easier route for the reaction, with a lower activation energy. Add this information to the diagram of the Maxwell–Boltzmann distribution then use collision theory to explain why the rate of reaction increases.

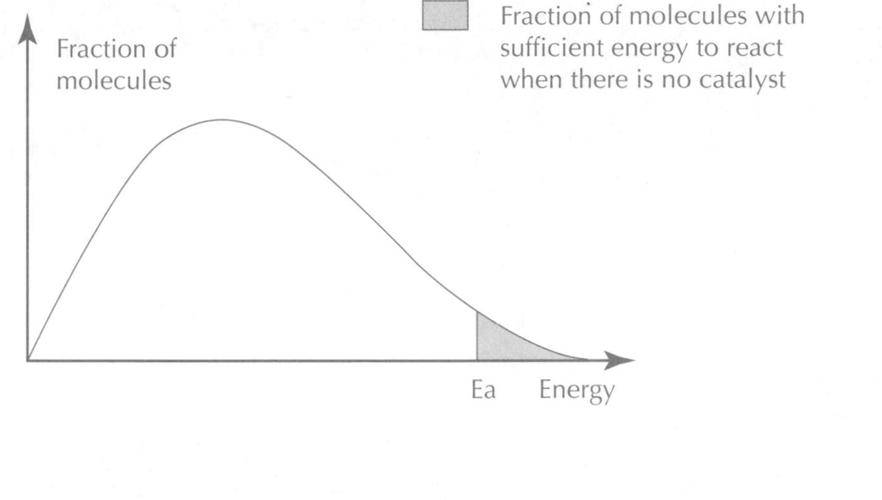

The effect of using a catalyst can also be shown on an enthalpy profile for a reaction.

On this enthalpy profile, sketch in the effect of using a catalyst.

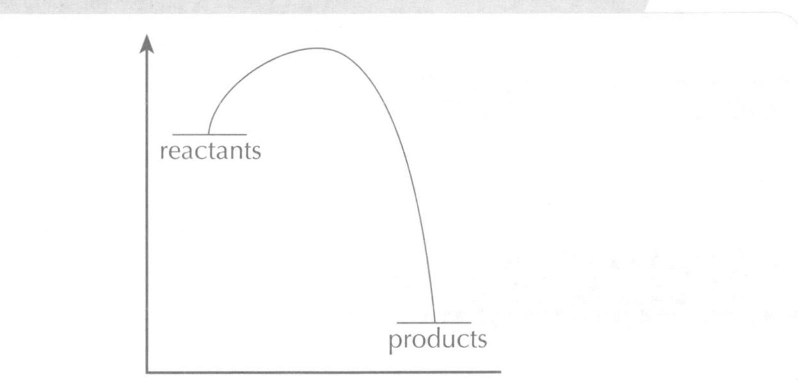

THE JARGON
In homogeneous catalysis the catalyst is in the same phase as the reactants, whereas in heterogeneous catalysis the catalyst and reactants are in different phases.

LINKS
For more detail on the effects of CFCs on ozone, see pp. 71–72.

Homogeneous catalysis

Give an example of homogeneous catalysis.

SYLLABUS CHECK
OCR, WJEC and CCEA only.

Heterogeneous catalysis

Iron is used in the Haber process for converting nitrogen and hydrogen to ammonia.

N2(g) 1 3H2(g) $\rightleftharpoons$ 2NH3(g)

Number the stages in this argument, which explains how the catalyst works.

- The molecules react to form NH_3 ☐
- This causes the reaction to have a high activation energy ☐
- The triple bond in nitrogen is very strong ☐
- The bonding is not so strong that it does not release the NH_3 gas formed ☐
- The bonding is strong enough to weaken bonds in H_2 and N_2 ☐
- H_2 and N_2 are adsorbed onto the iron surface ☐

THE JARGON
Adsorbed means the substance is taken up by the surface of the catalyst.

Turn the page for some exam questions on this topic ➤

For more on this topic, see pages 50–51 of the *Revision Express A-level Study Guide*

Exam question 1

Define the following terms.

Catalyst

SYLLABUS CHECK
AQA and Edexcel do not require you to know the terms homogeneous and heterogeneous at AS.

Homogeneous catalyst

Heterogeneous catalyst

Activation energy

Exam question 2

SYLLABUS CHECK
OCR needs this in detail and CCEA in outline.

An important application of catalysis is the removal of pollutants from car exhausts by catalytic converters. Write an account of this process. You should include details of the pollutants, the nature of the catalyst and its mode of action.

What are the pollutants?

How do they come to be in exhaust gases?

What is the nature of the catalyst?

How does the catalyst work? To give you a hint, it's a three-step process.

Write an equation for the reaction between CO and NO.

Equilibrium

Many reactions are reversible – they can go forwards and backwards. When a balance is reached between the rate of the forward reaction and the rate of the reverse reaction, we say that the system is in equilibrium.

SYLLABUS CHECK
CCEA students should make sure they can carry out calculations involving K_c and K_p. Other students will meet them next year.

DYNAMIC EQUILIBRIUM

In the contact process for the formation of sulphuric acid, one of the stages is the formation of SO_3 from SO_2; this is an equilibrium reaction.

Write an equation for this process. Include state symbols.

Put a tick against the boxes that contain true statements about this equilibrium.

- During the reaction, molecules of SO_2 and O_2 react to make SO_3 at the same time as SO_3 molecules decompose to make SO_2 and O_2 molecules ☐
- At equilibrium the forward and reverse reactions stop ☐
- At equilibrium the forward and reverse reactions are occurring at equal rates ☐
- At equilibrium there is no apparent change in the proportions of each gas present ☐
- Once equilibrium is reached, we cannot affect the position of equilibrium ☐
- A catalyst will alter the position of equilibrium and affect the yield of product ☐
- Catalysts do not affect the position of equilibrium; they just make the forward and reverse reactions occur faster ☐
- Equilibrium will be reached faster if a catalyst is used ☐
- A catalyst of vanadium(V) oxide is used in the contact process ☐
- Any statement can only be true if we are talking about a closed system ☐

THE JARGON
A closed system is one where no reactants or products can leave or enter the system.

LE CHATELIER'S PRINCIPLE

Le Chatelier stated that if a closed system in equilibrium is exposed to a change in conditions, then the position of equilibrium will alter in order to minimize the effect of that change.

The reaction $2SO_{2(g)} + O_{2(g)} \rightleftharpoons 2SO_{3(g)}$ is exothermic.

State whether the following changes would increase or decrease the yield of SO_3 and say why.

Increase the temperature (*T*)

Increase the pressure (*P*)

Use V_2O_5, a catalyst

Turn the page for some exam questions on this topic ➤

EXAM QUESTION 1

Use the steps below to develop your answer.

In the Haber process, nitrogen and hydrogen are reacted to form ammonia. Describe this process, paying particular attention to the conditions used in order to achieve a good yield of ammonia at a reasonable rate.

Write a balanced equation for this process, including state symbols.

Conditions for a fast rate

Say what conditions are needed to get a fast rate of reaction.

Conditions for a high yield

State and explain the conditions needed for a high yield. The reaction is exothermic.

Actual conditions

Give the actual conditions used in this process.

These conditions are used for the following reasons:

Why are these conditions used?

What is all the ammonia needed for?

Tick the boxes to show which of the following items are made from the ammonia obtained in the Haber process.

- Explosives ☐
- Natural gas ☐
- Fertilizers ☐
- Extracting aluminium ☐
- Polyamides like nylon ☐
- Sulphuric acid ☐

Acids and bases

A useful definition of an acid is a proton (H^+) donor, and a useful definition of a base is a proton acceptor. This is known as the Brønsted–Lowry theory.

SYLLABUS CHECK
The reactions of acids and bases are assumed knowledge from GCSE for most syllabuses, so it is a good idea to review them here. OCR lists these reactions on its syllabus.

STRONG AND WEAK ACIDS AND BASES

A strong acid fully dissociates into its ions but a weak acid only partially dissociates. A strong base fully dissociates into its ions but a weak base only partially dissociates.

For each equation, state whether the substance in bold is an acid or base and whether it is strong or weak.

$\mathbf{HCl_{(aq)}} \rightarrow H^+_{(aq)} + Cl^-_{(aq)}$

$\mathbf{NH_{3(aq)}} + H_2O_{(l)} \rightleftharpoons NH^+_{4(aq)} + OH^-_{(aq)}$

$\mathbf{NaOH_{(aq)}} \rightarrow Na^+_{(aq)} + OH^-_{(aq)}$

$\mathbf{CH_3CO_2H_{(aq)}} \rightleftharpoons CH_3CO^-_{2(aq)} + H^-_{(aq)}$

TYPICAL REACTIONS OF ACIDS AND BASES

Complete these general word equations.

ACID + METAL →

ACID + BASE →

ACID + ALKALI →

ACID + CARBONATE →

THE JARGON
An alkali is a soluble base; salts form when a metal displaces the hydrogen of an acid.

Write word equations for the following reactions. Do not learn specific equations; learn the general equations and apply them to specific cases.

magnesium + sulphuric acid →

copper (II) oxide + hydrochloric acid →

ammonia solution + sulphuric acid →

sodium carbonate + nitric acid →

General equation for neutralization of an acid by a base.

Whenever an acid reacts with a base, an ionic equation can be written that shows the hydrogen ion reacting with the hydroxide ion. Write this ionic equation.

When 50 cm³ of 2.0 mol dm^{-3} HCl react with 50 cm³ of 2.0 mol dm^{-3} NaOH, the temperature rises by 13.0 °C. Calculate $\Delta H_{neutralization}$

Energy given to solution =

Energy lost by chemical system =

Amount of acid =

Energy per mole of H^+ neutralized =

LINKS
For a reminder of how to calculate enthalpy changes, see p. 23.

WATCH OUT
When calculating enthalpies of neutralization, think carefully about the mass of solution that is heated.

Turn the page for some exam questions on this topic ➤

Exam question 1

One use for ammonia is to produce fertilizers. The ammonia is used as a source of the nitrogen needed for plant growth but ammonia itself is not applied directly to the soil; instead salts such as ammonium nitrate or ammonium sulphate are applied.

Write a balanced symbol equation for the reaction of ammonia with nitric acid to form ammonium nitrate, NH_4NO_3. Include state symbols.

SYLLABUS CHECK
AQA and Edexcel do not require you to know about Brønsted–Lowry theory.

How is ammonia acting as a Brønsted-Lowry base?

Write a balanced symbol equation for the reaction of ammonia to form ammonium sulphate, $(NH_4)_2SO_4$. Include state symbols.

Suggest two reasons why ammonia is not applied directly to fields.

How do the percentages (%) of nitrogen in ammonium nitrate and ammonium sulphate compare? Show your working. Use these values of A_r: N = 14.0, O ''' 16.0, H = 1.0, S = 32.1.

Find the molar mass of each and then calculate the percentage of this mass that is composed of nitrogen.

LINKS
To remind yourself of how to calculate molar mass, see p. 7.

DON'T FORGET
After you've calculated the percentages of nitrogen, make a comparison.

Redox reactions

Redox reactions occur when reduction and oxidation take place together. A substance that causes oxidation is an oxidizing agent and one that causes reduction is a reducing agent.

SYLLABUS CHECK
If you study CCEA, you also need to be able to use standard electrode potential values.

Assigning oxidation numbers

By assigning oxidation numbers (states) to elements, we can see whether oxidation or reduction has occurred.

Say whether these statements are true or false. If they are false, explain why. Check your answers before you move on to the next section.

In compounds, fluorine always has an oxidation number of +1

The oxidation number of an ion of an element is equal to its charge

In compounds, oxygen usually has an oxidation number of −2 and hydrogen +1

In complex ions the total of all the oxidation numbers is equal to the charge

When assigning oxidation numbers in a compound or complex ion, always assign the least electronegative atoms first

The oxidation number of all elements is 0

In metal hydrides, such as lithium hydride, hydrogen has an oxidation number of +1

LINKS
For a definition of electronegativity, see p. 11.

In each of these formulae, work out the oxidation state of the element in bold type.

$\mathbf{P}_2O_5$

$K\mathbf{Mn}O_4$

$\mathbf{Cr}Cl_3$

$K_2\mathbf{Cr}_2O_7$

$\mathbf{Cr}O_4^{2-}$

$Na\mathbf{H}$

THE JARGON
When hydrogen is combined with a metal, the compound is called a hydride.

Oxidation and reduction

Say whether these statements are true or false and if false, explain why.

Oxidation number increases when oxidation occurs

Oxidation number decreases when reduction occurs

Electrons are lost during oxidation and electrons are gained during reduction

SPEED LEARNING
OILRIG: **o**xidation **i**s **l**oss of electrons, **r**eduction **i**s **g**ain of electrons.

When Cr reacts with Cl_2 we can see that redox is occurring because the oxidation number of Cr goes *up* from 0 to +3; the oxidation number of Cl_2 goes *down* from 0 to −1.

Write a balanced equation for this reaction; label the oxidation states on Cr and Cl. Indicate the reduction and oxidation with labelled arrows.

Turn the page for some exam questions on this topic ➤

Exam question 1

The reaction of NO and CO brought about by the catalytic converter in a car exhaust is a redox reaction. The products are nitrogen and carbon dioxide. Write a balanced equation for this reaction and identify the substance that is oxidized.

You can do this most easily by looking at which substance gains oxygen.

Exam question 2

SYLLABUS CHECK
Only AQA needs you to know that titration is a method of determining the amount of iodine present, but all boards except OCR require you to add half-equations like this.

During the titration of I_2 with sodium thiosulphate, $Na_2S_2O_3$, the endpoint is detected when the iodine has all been reduced to I^- ions. The thiosulphate is oxidized to the tetrathionate ion, $S_4O_6^{2-}$.

Write an ion/electron equation for the reduction of iodine.

This is a half-equation.

The ion/electron equation for the oxidation is

$$2S_2O_3^{2-} \rightarrow S_4O_6^{2-} + 2e^- .$$

Show that the sulphur has been oxidized.

Look at oxidation numbers.

Combine the two equations to write a fully balanced ionic equation for the reaction.

First make sure there is an equal number of electrons in both equations, multiplying any equation as necessary.

Then combine the equations so the electrons cancel out.

WATCH OUT
If you have correctly combined the equations, make sure the atoms balance and the charges balance.

Exam question 3

These equations show three displacement reactions of the halogens:

$$Cl_{2\,(aq)} + 2KBr_{(aq)} \rightarrow 2KCl_{(aq)} + Br_{2\,(aq)}$$

$$Br_{2\,(aq)} + 2KI_{(aq)} \rightarrow 2KBr_{(aq)} + I_{2\,(aq)}$$

$$Cl_{2\,(aq)} + 2KI_{(aq)} \rightarrow 2KCl_{(aq)} + I_{2\,(aq)}$$

What do they show about the oxidizing ability of the halogens?

Look at what happens to the oxidation numbers.

The periodic table

The periodic table is a wonderful tool for chemists, and it's a shame to put it so far into this book. But now you've reached it!

How the periodic table is organized

The periodic table shows all the elements in order of atomic number with an overlying arrangement of elements into vertical groups and horizontal periods.

Add labels for groups 1 to 0; periods 1, 2, 3 and the transition metals. Shade the s block, p block and d block in different colours and add a key below the table.

		H						He
Li	Be		B	C	N	O	F	Ne
Na	Mg		Al	Si	P	S	Cl	Ar
K	Ca		Ga	Ge	As	Se	Br	Kr
Rb	Sr		In	Sn	Sb	Te	I	Xe

Key

Trends across a period

There are repeating trends in physical and chemical properties across a period.

Give each of these graphs a title to show what trend it shows. Choose from these four options: electrical conductivity across period 3, melting point across period 3, atomic radius down group 2, atomic radius across period 3.

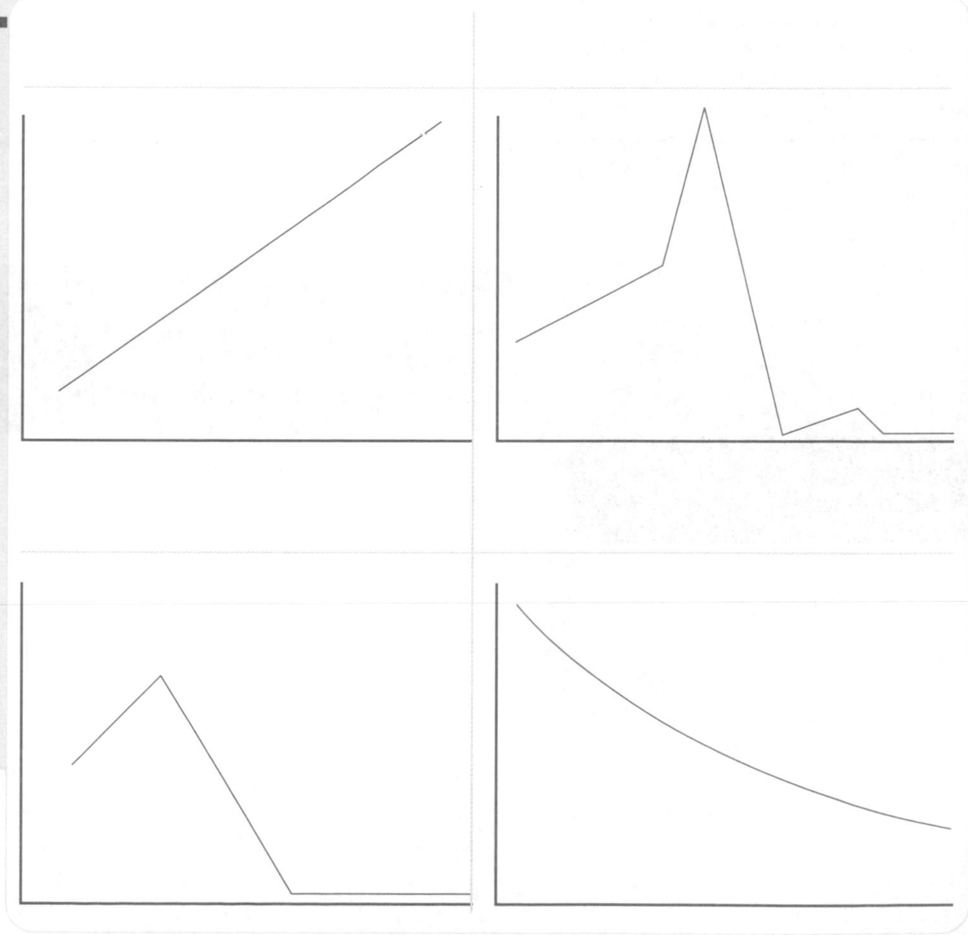

Turn the page for some exam questions on this topic ➤

For more on this topic, see pages 88–89 of the *Revision Express A-level Study Guide*

Exam question 1

Here is some data about the elements of period 3.

T_B is the boiling point in kelvin and r_A is the atomic radius in nanometres.

	Na	Mg	Al	Si	P	S	Cl	Ar
T_B (K)	371	922	933	1683	317	386	172	84
r_A (nm)	0.191	0.160	0.130	0.118	0.110	0.102	0.099	0.095

Describe and explain the trend in atomic radius across the period.

WATCH OUT

The question asks you to describe *and* explain. Don't forget to do both.

THE JARGON

Screening, sometimes known as shielding, is due to the repulsive effect of electrons. Inner shell electrons will have a repulsive effect on electrons entering an outer shell. The outer electrons are screened from the full attractive force of the nucleus.

The atomic radius

because the nuclear charge

so the attraction between electrons and nucleus

but the amount of screening

Describe and explain the change in melting point across the period.

When you are asked about melting point, you should link it to structure and bonding. Fill in this table to show the information you would use in your answer.

	Bonding and structure	Effect on melting point
Na to Al		
Si		
P to Cl		
Ar		

WATCH OUT

The strength of van der Waals forces depends on the number of electrons. S_8 has the most, then P_4, Cl_2 and lastly Ar. This explains the shape of the graph you labelled on p. 35.

Exam question 2

For each description, state the type of structure and bonding present.

You should be able to interpret data given in terms of the structure and bonding present. Use *all* of the data.

Melts at 698 °C; conducts when molten but not when solid

Melts at 101 °C; does not dissolve in water or conduct

Melts at 1 610 °C; hard, does not dissolve, does not conduct.

Melts at 1 660 °C; conducts when solid

Interpreting ionization energies

By looking at the way in which ionization energies change, we can use the information to justify the existence of subshells and work out what group an element is in.

TREND ACROSS A PERIOD

DON'T FORGET
Your definition should contain the words 'gaseous' and 'one mole'.

The first ionization energy of an element is the energy required to remove one mole of electrons from one mole of the gaseous atoms.

$$M_{(g)} \rightarrow M^{+}_{(g)} + e^{-}$$

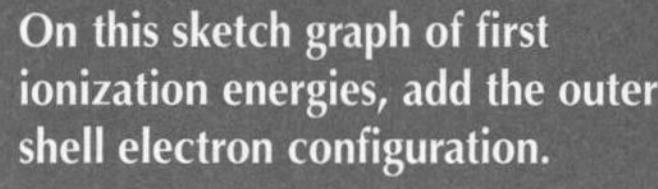

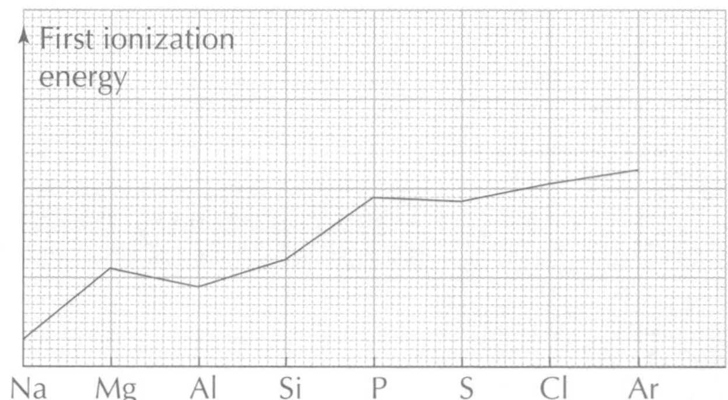

LINKS
To remind yourself about the basics of ionization energies, see p. 9.

Explain how each of these three factors affects first ionization energy.

Nuclear charge

Distance from nucleus

Screening

DON'T FORGET
It is the outer electron that's removed.

Say whether each of these statements is true or false. If it is false, explain why.

Going down a group, the ionization energy decreases due to increased distance from the nucleus and extra shielding.

The electrons in boxes notation for the outer electrons of Al, P and S is correctly shown below.

P $[Ne]3s^23p^3$ S $[Ne]3s^23p^4$

3s 3p 3s 3p 3s 3p

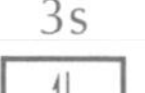

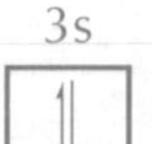

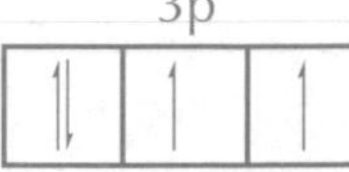

The first ionization energy of Al is lower than Mg because the 3p orbital is at a higher energy level than the 3s.

The first ionization energy of S is lower than P because the repulsion caused by spin pairing in the 3p orbital makes it easier to remove this electron.

Turn the page for some exam questions on this topic ➤

For more on this topic, see page 88 of the *Revision Express A-level Study Guide*

THE JARGON
Successive ionization energies are for removal of second and subsequent electrons from the gaseous ion.

DON'T FORGET
Ionization energies are always endothermic.

EXAM QUESTION 1

This data shows successive ionization energies for a number of different elements. Study the data then answer the questions.

	Successive ionization energy (kJ mol^{-1})					
	First	Second	Third	Fourth	Fifth	Sixth
P	419	3 051	4 412	5 877	7 975	9 649
Q	1 012	1 903	2 912	4 957	6 274	21 269
R	496	4 563	6 913	9 544	13 352	16 611
S	578	1 817	2 745	11 578	14 831	18 378

Write an equation to show the first ionization energy for P.

Write an equation to show the second ionization energy for Q.

Write an equation to show the third ionization energy for R.

How much energy is needed to form a mole of $S^{2+}_{(g)}$ from $S_{(g)}$?

Will this value have a positive or negative sign?

Which element is in group 5? Explain your reasoning.

Which two elements are in the same group of the periodic table?

Group 1 – the alkali metals

The elements lithium to caesium in group 1 of the periodic table are soft reactive metals with low melting points. Their characteristic flame colours can be used in analysis.

SYLLABUS CHECK
Although the specific information here is only needed by Edexcel (and a little for CCEA), the general principles discussed apply to group 2 as well.

SYLLABUS CHECK
This is the only aspect of group 1 covered by CCEA.

Flame colours

When compounds containing these elements are heated, the electrons of the metals become excited and are raised into higher energy levels. When the electrons drop back down to their original energy level, they emit the energy as light of specific wavelengths.

Match the flame colour to the metal.

1 lithium	yellow-orange
2 sodium	lilac
3 potassium	brilliant red

Reactions of the elements with oxygen

The elements of group 1 all react with oxygen by losing their outer electron and making oxides. Reactivity increases down the group.

Complete these equations to show the formation of the oxides.

$4\,Li_{(s)} + O_{2(g)} \rightarrow$	oxide
$2Na_{(s)} + O_{2(g)} \rightarrow$	peroxide
$K_{(s)} + O_{2(g} \rightarrow$	superoxide

THE JARGON
Sodium forms the peroxide (O_2^{2-} ion). Potassium forms the superoxide (O_2^- ion).

Reactions of the elements with water

The elements all behave in a similar way to each other, forming hydrogen and alkaline solutions. Reactivity increases down the group.

Write an equation for the reaction of a typical alkali metal, M, with water.

LINKS
For a reminder of the reaction between acids and bases, see p. 31.

Reaction of the oxides with water and dilute acid

The oxides react with water to form hydroxides and with acids to form the relevant salt and water.

Write an equation to show the reaction of lithium oxide with water.

Write an equation to show the reaction of Na_2O with dilute sulphuric acid.

THE JARGON
The polarizing ability is the ability of the cation to distort anions.

Thermal stability of the nitrates and carbonates

The thermal stability of the nitrates and carbonates increases as you go down group 1; this is because the polarizing ability of the cation decreases down the group. Group 1 carbonates, except lithium carbonate, are stable to heat but the nitrates decompose.

For each of these statements, say whether the ability of the cation to polarize the anion will increase or decrease.

Factor increased	Effect on how well cation can polarize
Size of the cation	
Charge on the cation	
Size of the anion	

Turn the page for some exam questions on this topic ➤

Exam question 1

A group 1 metal (A) is heated in air and rapidly oxidizes, burning with a yellow/orange flame and forming a white solid (B). Water is dripped onto the white solid and an exothermic reaction occurs. Continued addition of water causes a new substance (C) to dissolve. The resulting solution is titrated with nitric acid using an indicator to show when neutralization is complete. The neutral solution contains a salt (D). When a solution of this salt is heated in an evaporating dish to obtain the solid, it decomposes and releases a colourless gas that relights a glowing splint leaving a white solid (E).

Identify substances A to E.

Write four symbol equations for the formation of products B to E.

DON'T FORGET
Sodium nitrite also forms.

Exam question 2

(a) Describe and explain the trend in the ease of decomposition of the nitrates of group 1.
(b) Write symbolic equations to show the decomposition of potassium nitrate and lithium nitrate.

First describe ...

then explain ... think in terms of the size and charge of the metal ion as you go down the group.

Now write the equations. Lithium, being at the top of group 1, is very polarizing and causes a greater amount of disruption to the nitrate ion than potassium.

Group 2

The elements of group 2 are fairly reactive metals; they form compounds in which the oxidation state is +2. Like group 1, they can be identified in compounds from their flame colours.

SYLLABUS CHECK
Flame tests are not needed by OCR.

Flame colours

○○○

Match the colour to the metal.

1 calcium	apple green
2 strontium	crimson
3 barium	brick red

SYLLABUS CHECK
If you follow the AQA syllabus, you should check your knowledge of the atypical behaviour of $BeCl_2$ and $Be(OH)_2$.

Reaction of the metal with oxygen and water

○○○

All produce ionic oxides when they are burned. Ca, Sr and Ba react with water with increasing vigour, forming hydrogen and alkaline solutions. Mg reacts with steam to form the oxide and hydrogen.

Write general equations for the reactions of a group 2 metal, M, with oxygen and water.

LINKS
For a reminder of the reaction between metals and acids, see p. 31.

Reaction of magnesium and its compounds with acid

○○○

You need to know about the reactions of Mg, MgO, $Mg(OH)_2$ and $MgCO_3$ with dilute hydrochloric acid.

Thermal stability of group 2 nitrates and carbonates

○○○

What is this trend and how can it be explained?

THE JARGON
As you go down the group, the ionic radius increases, so the +2 charge is spread over a greater volume. We say the charge density has decreased.

LINKS
The thermal stabilities of group 2 nitrates and carbonates show the same trend as those of group 1, as shown on p. 39.

Carbonates decompose to the oxide and carbon dioxide.
Nitrates decompose to NO_2 and O_2.

Solubility trends of the hydroxides and sulphates

○○○

Are these statements true or false? If they are false, explain why.

As you go down group 2, the solubility of the hydroxide decreases

As you go down group 2, the solubility of the sulphate decreases

Insolubility of $BaSO_4$ is used to identify Ba^{2+} ions and SO_4^{2-} ions

$Mg(OH)_2$ is not very soluble and does not form many OH^- ions in solution; $Ba(OH)_2$ is much more soluble and forms more OH^- ions in solution

Turn the page for some exam questions on this topic ➤

For more on this topic, see pages 90–91 of the *Revision Express A-level Study Guide*

Exam question 1

A student wanted to compare the reactivity of magnesium, calcium and strontium, so they reacted a small piece of each with oxygen, cold water and dilute hydrochloric acid. Complete this results table to say what would have occurred.

DON'T FORGET
Write down all the things you would *see*. Give the identity of any gases formed.

	Held in Bunsen flame	Reaction dropped in cold water	Reaction dropped in acid
Mg			
Ca			
Sr			

Exam question 2

The trends in behaviour of group 2 metals and their compounds can be explained using a few core ideas A, B, C. As you go down the group:

A the outer electron configuration is always s^2
B the distance of the outer electron from the nucleus increases
C the charge density on the cation decreases

For each of these five trends, say whether A, B or C is responsible.

DON'T FORGET
There is one trend you do not have to explain, the trend in the solubilities of the hydroxides and sulphates.

The reactivity increases as you go down the group	☐
The thermal stability of nitrates and carbonates increases as you go down the group	☐
They all show a +2 oxidation state	☐
Decrease in first ionization energy	☐
Decrease in melting point of the oxides from MgO to BaO	☐

Exam question 3

$Mg(NO_3)_2$ and $MgCO_3$ decompose relatively easily on heating. Write balanced equations, with state symbols, to show this.

DON'T FORGET
You've probably done this in the laboratory; think back over what happened and it may help you write the equations.

Limestone – calcium carbonate

Calcium carbonate gives us the warm yellow of a Cotswold limestone and the white cliffs of Dover, but it's got much more than just a pretty face.

Decomposition of limestone

This process has been carried out for centuries in limekilns and cement works throughout the world. The $CaCO_3$ is heated strongly to bring about its decomposition.

For each of these processes, write in the product name, its formula and its state.

Process	Product	Trivial name	Formula and state
Heating $CaCO_3$		quicklime	
Adding water to quicklime		slaked lime	
Dissolving the quicklime completely		limewater solution	

Reactions of limewater

Limewater is the test for carbon dioxide gas, but how does it work? Calcium hydroxide solution has a pH of about 11 and will absorb acidic gases such as CO_2. In doing so, it goes milky as solid $CaCO_3$ forms, but if excess CO_2 is passed through, it becomes clear again as the $CaCO_3$ redissolves to form calcium hydrogencarbonate.

Complete these word and symbol equations.

calcium hydroxide + carbon dioxide → +

 + $CO_{2(g)}$ → +

calcium carbonate + carbon dioxide + water → calcium hydrogencarbonate

This last reaction is what causes caves to form in limestone regions. Rain, with dissolved carbon dioxide, dissolves the limestone and carries it away as a solution of calcium hydrogencarbonate.

What happens when you boil water with Ca^{2+} ions in it?

Turn the page for some exam questions on this topic ➤

Exam question 1

The compounds of group 2 elements are put to various uses. For each of the compounds listed below, give a use and explain the chemistry behind it.

THE JARGON
A suspension is a mixture of liquid and tiny particles of solid, which remain suspended rather than settling out quickly.

	Use	Chemistry behind use
Magnesium hydroxide suspension		
Calcium carbonate		
Aqueous calcium hydroxide		
Solid calcium hydroxide		

Exam question 2

Some data books on analysis write the following:

Ion	Test. Add NaOH, first dropwise then to excess
Ba^{2+}	No precipitate provided reagents are pure

A technician makes up the solutions from 100% pure $BaCl_2$ and deionized water before a practical exam and uses the NaOH solution from the reagent cupboard, but they cannot get the test to behave as it should. The solution keeps going cloudy. Using your knowledge of the group 2 solubility trend, see if you can help them.

Is barium hydroxide soluble?

If the NaOH solution is not completely fresh, is there anything it might have reacted with?

When the NaOH reacts with CO_2, what solution does it form?

You often see a white crust of this around the tops of NaOH bottles that haven't been used for a while.

Suggest an identity for the technician's precipitate and write an ionic equation for its formation.

Use what you know about the trend in solubilities of the sulphates and assume this holds for the carbonates.

The behaviour of group 7 – the halogens

The halogens are all non-metals and they show clear trends in their physical and chemical behaviour.

Trend in volatility

This graph shows how the boiling points of the halogens vary. Explain the variation in boiling point shown by the halogens.

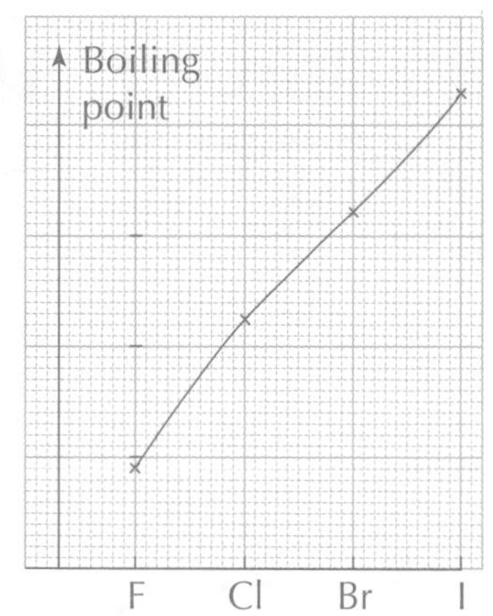

THE JARGON
Volatility describes the ease with which a substance forms a vapour.

Displacement reactions

As you go down the group, the reactivity of the halogens decreases.

Complete these ionic equations to show displacement reactions of the halogens. If no reaction occurs, write 'no reaction'.

$Cl_{2(g)} + 2Br^-_{(aq)} \rightarrow$

$Br_{2(aq)} + 2Cl^-_{(aq)} \rightarrow$

$Br_{2(aq)} + 2I^-_{(aq)} \rightarrow$

$I_{2(aq)} + 2Cl^-_{(aq)} \rightarrow$

SYLLABUS CHECK
Displacement by chlorine is mentioned by Edexcel as a means of obtaining bromine from seawater.

Tick which of these explanations correctly explains the statement. If it is incorrect explain why.

Correct statement	Explanation	
The halide ions show an oxidation number of −1 in their compounds with metals	Their outer electron arrangement is s^2p^5 and they gain one electron from metals when they react	
Hydrogen halide solutions are acidic	When they dissolve in water they release OH^- ions	
Chlorine is a better oxidizing agent than bromine	Chlorine can gain electrons more readily than bromine	
When concentrated sulphuric acid is added to solid halides, sodium chloride releases HCl but sodium iodide releases I_2	An iodide ion is less easily oxidized than a chloride ion	
Iodide ions are better reducing agents than chloride ions	Iodide ions more readily lose electrons than chloride ions	

SPEED LEARNING
OILRIG: **o**xidation **i**s **l**oss of electrons, **r**eduction **i**s **g**ain of electrons.

DON'T FORGET
A good oxidizing agent will always be easily reduced.

Turn the page for some exam questions on this topic ➤

Exam question 1

A student has three solutions, P, Q and R, which they know are halides. First they are given silver nitrate solution and dilute ammonia solution. Describe how they would carry out a test to distinguish them and state what they would observe with each halide.

What test would they do?

Complete the table.

Halide present	Observation
Cl^-	
Br^-	
I^-	

THE JARGON
ppt. is short for precipitate. This is when two solutions are added and a solid forms.

Next the student is told to identify solutions P, Q and R by using solutions of Cl_2, Br_2 and I_2. Unfortunately, the label has fallen off the solutions of Cl_2 and I_2. Using only litmus paper, how could they distinguish the solutions of Cl_2 and I_2?

Now the student has positively identified each halogen solution, they carry out the following tests with the following results. Read these results then identify each solution explaining your reasoning.

Test carried out	Result
1 Cl_2 water mixed with each halide solution in turn	P and Q became darker R did not change
2 Starch solution added to solutions from test 1	Q immediately turned blue-black P and R did not change

Start with R.

Now distinguish between P and Q.

Reactions of group 7

Here we look at some reactions of group 7 that hinge around redox reactions.

HALIDES WITH CONCENTRATED SULPHURIC ACID

The reducing ability of halide ions increases down the group. This is seen when concentrated sulphuric acid is added to a solid halide.

Complete the conclusion column.

Observation when concentrated sulphuric acid is added to the solid halide	Conclusion Halide ion present
A brown gas forms which turns damp blue litmus paper red	
Violet vapour forms immediately	
Gas formed which turns damp blue litmus paper red but does not bleach it. It forms white clouds with NH_3 gas	

REACTION OF Cl_2 WITH WATER

Chlorine disproportionates when it reacts with water, forming the chloride ion and chloric(I) acid.

Add the oxidation states above chlorine and then add labelled arrows to show the disproportionation.

$$Cl_{2(g)} + H_2O_{(l)} \rightarrow Cl^-_{(aq)} + HClO_{(aq)} + H^+_{(aq)}$$

THE JARGON
Disproportionation occurs when a substance is simultaneously oxidized and reduced.

Chlorine is used in this way in water sterilization. The chloric(I) acid is a strong oxidizing agent and kills bacteria.

REACTION OF Cl_2 WITH SODIUM HYDROXIDE

Only two of these equations are correct and are correctly described in terms of redox. Put a tick beside them.

Equation	Description	
$Cl_2 + 2NaOH \rightarrow NaCl + NaClO + H_2$	Cold; Cl oxidized only	
$3NaClO \rightarrow NaCl + NaClO_3$	Cold; Cl disproportionates	
$Cl_2 + 2NaOH \rightarrow NaCl + NaClO + H_2$	Hot; Cl disproportionates	
$3NaClO \rightarrow 2NaCl + NaClO_3$	Hot; Cl disproportionates	
$Cl_2 + 2NaOH \rightarrow 2NaCl + NaClO + H_2$	Cold; Cl disproportionates	
$3NaClO \rightarrow NaCl + NaClO_3$	Hot; Cl reduced only	

SYLLABUS CHECK
Only Edexcel and CCEA require the reaction with hot NaOH to make chlorate(V).

You need to learn the two correct equations and their descriptions. One of these is the reaction that the membrane cell is designed to avoid.

LINKS
To see how the membrane cell works, have a look at p. 49.

Turn the page for some exam questions on this topic ➤

EXAM QUESTION 1

Household bleaches often contain sodium chlorate(I). A student wants to find the concentration of this in a commercially available bleach. They have carried out an experiment to estimate the amount of ClO^- in each, using the fact that it will release iodine when reacted with potassium iodide solution. The amount of iodine released can then be found by performing a titration with a standard solution of sodium thiosulphate. Here are the half-equations for these reactions:

$$ClO^-_{(aq)} + 2H^+_{(aq)} + 2e^- \rightarrow C^-_{(aq)} + H_2O_{(l)}$$

$$I_{2\,(aq)} + 2e^- \rightarrow 2I^-_{(aq)}$$

$$S_4O_6^{2-}{}_{(aq)} + 2e^- \rightarrow 2S_2O_3^{2-}{}_{(aq)}$$

DON'T FORGET

When combining a pair of half-equations, one is written as a forward reaction and the other as the reverse reaction. When they're added together, the electrons cancel out.

Use the half-equations to write a balanced equation for each reaction.

What indicator would be used and what would happen at the endpoint?

For each bleach, 5.0 cm³ were placed into a 100 cm³ volumetric flask, which was then topped up with deionized water. A 10.0 cm³ sample of bleach A was removed and reacted with an excess of acidified potassium iodide solution. The resulting iodine needed 15.00 cm³ of 0.10 mol dm⁻³ sodium thiosulphate to react fully. Calculate the concentration of ClO^- in bleach A.

Calculate the number of moles of thiosulphate used in the titration.

From the equations, find the ratio of $S_2O_3^{2-}$, I_2 and ClO^- in order to find the number of moles of ClO^- in the 10.0 cm³ sample.

How much ClO^- was in the volumetric flask in total?

What was the concentration of the original bleach?

Industrial extractions

This section looks at four important industrial processes. Look carefully at the syllabus checks.

SYLLABUS CHECK
AQA only for iron extraction.

Extracting iron

Iron is extracted in a high-temperature continuous process in a blast furnace; the raw materials are

Name the raw materials.

Coke burns to form CO_2 exothermically; this heats the furnace:

Write the equation here.

The CO_2 then reacts with more carbon:

Write the equation here.

Both CO and C can act as reducing agents in different parts of the furnace but the main reducing agent is CO:

Write two equations to show reduction of iron oxide by C and by CO.

Limestone ($CaCO_3$) is added to remove sandy impurities as liquid slag. It decomposes into CaO; the CaO reacts to remove SiO_2:

Write an equation for SiO_2 removal.

Other wastes are oxides of carbon and, if sulphide ores are used, sulphur dioxide gas.

SYLLABUS CHECK
Edexcel requires you to know principles of the membrane cell.

Electrolysis of brine

Put these labels onto the diagram of the membrane cell in the correct place: chlorine, hydrogen, $Na^+_{(aq)}$ moves through, anode, cathode, brine in, spent brine out, dil. $NaOH_{(aq)}$ in, conc. $NaOH_{(aq)}$ out.

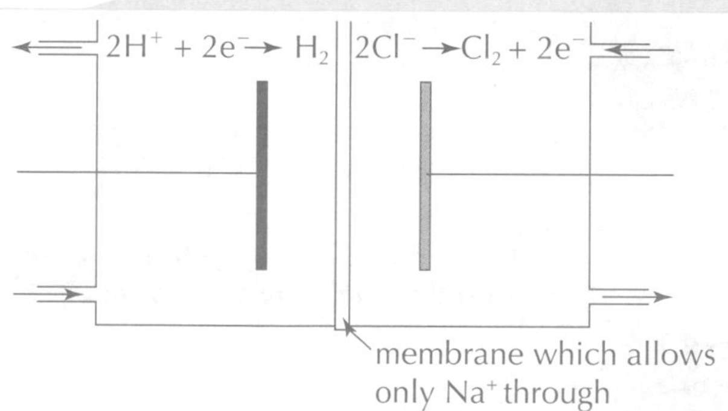

SYLLABUS CHECK
AQA only.

Extraction of titanium

Titanium is the ninth most abundant element in the Earth's crust but it is very expensive. This is down to the high costs of extraction.

Shade in three different colours to link the process in the first column, the equation in the second and the comment in the third. The first column shows the processes in the correct order.

First titanium oxide is converted to its chloride	$TiCl_{4(l)} + 2Mg_{(l)} \rightarrow Ti_{(s)} + 2MgCl_{2(l)}$	At 700 °C under an inert Ar atmosphere
Then titanium chloride is reduced using Mg or Na	$TiO_{2(s)} + 2Cl_{2(g)} + 2C_{(s)} \rightarrow TiCl_{4(l)} + 2CO_{(g)}$	Electrolysis
Mg is reclaimed from the $MgCl_2$ so it can be used again	$MgCl_{2(l)} \rightarrow Mg_{(l)} + Cl_{2(g)}$	Heating with carbon and chlorine

Turn the page for some exam questions on this topic ➤

SYLLABUS CHECK
Question 1 for Edexcel only but question 2 for all exam boards.

EXAM QUESTION 1

This question concerns the extraction of aluminium from its ore, bauxite.

(a) Outline the purification of aluminium oxide; include an explanation of the chemistry involved. Equations are not required for the purification.

(b) Outline the electrolysis of aluminium oxide. Give equations for the electrode reactions and state and explain the conditions used.

The statements explain how the aluminium oxide is purified. Number the statements to get them in the right order.

- This means that the impurities can be filtered off ☐
- Aluminium oxide is amphoteric and dissolves in NaOH solution ☐
- The impurities are insoluble in NaOH solution ☐
- The solution after filtration contains the aluminate ion ☐
- A small amount of pure aluminium oxide is added, which causes precipitation of the oxide ☐
- Bauxite is Al_2O_3 with impurities like iron oxide and silica ☐

THE JARGON
Amphoteric means that it will react with both acids and alkalis.

What ions are present in aluminium oxide?

First the pure oxide must be made molten but the melting point is 2045 °C. Why is it so high and how is it lowered?

What occurs at the cathode?

What occurs at the anode?

This is unfortunate for the carbon anode. Why is that?

EXAM QUESTION 2

If 102 kg of Al_2O_3 are electrolysed, what mass of Al and what volume of O_2, measured at STP, would be formed? (Al = 27, O =16)

Calculate moles of Al_2O_3 then write a balanced equation.

How many moles of Al come from 1 mole of Al_2O_3?

How many kilograms of Al form?

What volume of O_2 forms?

DON'T FORGET
1 mole of any gas at STP occupies 22.4 dm^3.

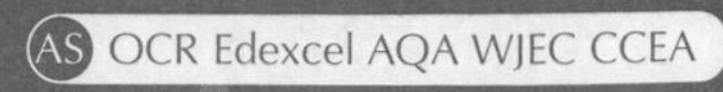

Organic chemistry – the basics

This section introduces some of the basic ideas that you need for the rest of the book.

DIFFERENT TYPES OF FORMULA

Draw the example in the third column using the rules in the second.

General formula of alkanes	Used to represent any member of a homologous series (see below)	
Molecular formula of ethanol	Shows the number of each type of atom in the compound	
Structural formula of ethanol	The minimal amount of detail that allows an unambiguous formula to be worked out	
Displayed formula of ethanoic acid	Shows the relative placing and number of bonds between atoms	
Skeletal formula of butane	Hydrogen atoms are removed to leave a carbon skeleton and functional groups	

Three terms are defined: nomenclature, functional group, homologous series. Write the correct term beside its definition.

	A series of compounds with the same functional group where each member increases by $-CH_2-$ and which can be described by a general formula
	A system of naming compounds. You should use IUPAC rules
	The part of a molecule that dictates its chemical behaviour

THE JARGON
IUPAC stands for International Union of Pure and Applied Chemistry.

TYPES OF REACTION

Beside each description, state the type of reaction. Choose your answers from these words: hydrolysis, elimination, oxidation, electrophilic, free, radical, addition, nucleophilic, substitution, reduction.

	Where attack is by a species with an unpaired electron
	Two species add to each other
	Swapping one species for another
	One species breaks down to two
	When water breaks open a bond
	Gain of hydrogen or loss of oxygen
	Gain of oxygen or loss of hydrogen
	Where the reagent is attracted by negative charge in the target molecule
	Where the reagent is attracted by positive charge in the target molecule

Turn the page for some exam questions on this topic ➤

Exam question 1

LINKS
You may need to look at p. 59 in order to answer these questions.

This question concerns the linear molecule, C_4H_8.

What functional group does it contain?

What is its general formula?

What is the next member of this homologous series?

THE JARGON
Structural isomerism occurs when compounds have the same molecular formula but different structural formulae.

Draw displayed formulae for two straight-chain structural isomers of C_4H_8 and name them.

THE JARGON
In alkenes, *cis / trans* isomerism occurs when there is at least one double bond in a molecule. There must be two different groups attached at either end of the double bond.

Draw the displayed formula for another structural isomer of C_4H_8 that does not show *cis / trans* isomerism and explain why it doesn't.

Draw and name the *cis / trans* isomers of but-2-ene.

Alkanes

The simplest of organic compounds, the alkanes are saturated hydrocarbons and show very limited chemistry.

Why are alkanes so unreactive?

All these statements are true. Tick the two statements that together explain the unreactivity of alkanes.

1. All alkanes contain strong covalent bonds ☐
2. The covalent bonds are not at all polar because the electronegativity of C and H is so similar ☐
3. Van der Waals' forces are stronger when molecules can approach more closely ☐
4. Van der Waals forces become larger as the number of electrons increases ☐
5. There are only van der Waals forces holding individual molecules together ☐
6. Alkanes do not attract nucleophiles or electrophiles ☐

What property is explained by statement 5? Which statement explains why the boiling point of alkanes increases with increased chain length? Which one explains why branched alkanes have lower boiling points than their straight-chain counterparts?

Alkanes have two main types of reaction. What are they?

SYLLABUS CHECK
Edexcel does not require any mechanisms.

Mechanism of free radical substitution

INITIATION

Chlorine molecules absorb energy from ultraviolet light and undergo homolytic fission:

Write the equation.

THE JARGON
Homolytic fission is when the single bond is broken and one electron goes onto each chlorine, forming two free radicals Cl·.

PROPAGATION

The chlorine free radical attacks methane, pulling off a hydrogen and its electron and leaving a methyl free radical:

Write the equation.

The free radical is regenerated when the CH_3· free radical attacks another chlorine molecule:

Write the equation.

The propagation steps repeat many times, only stopping when termination occurs.

TERMINATION

Two free radicals combine to form a molecule, e.g.

Write the equation.

Turn the page for some exam questions on this topic ➤

SYLLABUS CHECK
Edexcel does not require any mechanisms.

Exam question 1

The photochlorination of methane by a free radical mechanism can lead to the formation of CH_2Cl_2 and CCl_4. Draw out a sequence of steps that show how CH_2Cl_2 could form, starting with Cl_2 and CH_4.

Initiation

Propagation

Termination

Exam question 2

Methane, propane and butane are all used as fuels around the house and garden. Write equations for the complete combustion of all three and say why these reactions are exothermic.

LINKS
For a reminder of bond energies, see p. 22.

Exam question 3

A sample of an alkane undergoes complete combustion. The products were collected at RTP and were found to be 1.44 dm^3 of CO_2 and 1.26 g of water. Calculate the empirical formula of the alkane. (C = 12, H = 1.0, O = 16)

LINKS
For information on the volume of 1 mole of gas at RTP, see p. 7

Calculate moles of H_2O and hence H.

Caculate moles of CO_2 and hence C.

Find simplest ratio of these.

If M_r = 86, what is the molecular formula?

Making the most of crude oil

The source of hydrocarbons is crude oil but this must be processed before anything useful can be done with it.

SYLLABUS CHECK
OCR and AQA cover this topic in rather more depth than other syllabuses; check yours to see what you can miss out.

FRACTIONAL DISTILLATION

This is the first process carried out on crude oil. The mixture of hydrocarbons is heated and fractions are separated depending on the size of the carbon chain.

Why does this process work?

CRACKING

After fractional distillation the volume of each product obtained does not match the demand for it. Cracking breaks larger molecules into smaller ones, which are more in demand. This requires high temperature and pressure and it occurs by a free radical mechanism.

What else is obtained by cracking?

Thermal cracking produces a large proportion of alkenes

If C_9H_{20} is cracked and one of the two products is C_6H_{14}, write a balanced equation for the reaction; name both products.

Why are such high temperatures required?

If this is a free radical mechanism, will it be homolytic or heterolytic bond fission?

CATALYTIC CRACKING

THE JARGON
Zeolites are a group of minerals. They are used in ion exchange columns, for water purification.

If cracking is carried out with a zeolite catalyst, at fairly high temperatures but lower pressures, the products contain a higher proportion of cycloalkanes and arenes. These are desirable for the most efficient burning of petrol.

ISOMERIZATION AND REFORMING

Alternatively, two other processes are carried out to convert straight-chain alkanes: isomerization and reforming.

Read the descriptions and write in the name beside each process.

Straight-chain compounds are converted to branched-chain compounds

Conversion to cycloalkanes and arenes

Turn the page for some exam questions on this topic ➤

For more on this topic, see page 164 of the *Revision Express A-level Study Guide*

Exam question 1

Fractional distillation is the first process in refining crude oil. Read the questions in the margin then answer in the spaces provided.

The diagram shows a fractionating column. What property of the hydrocarbons allows them to be separated in this way?

The molecules can be separated because

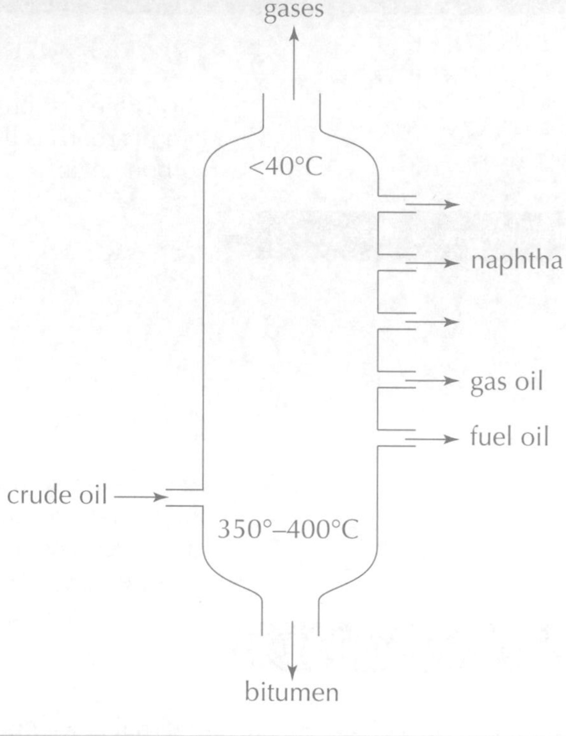

Label the missing fractions.

Label the number of carbon atoms present in molecules of the petrol fraction.

Cracking may be carried out on the alkanes obtained from fractional distillation. Why is this necessary?

Cracking is necessary because

Octane ratings for petrol are based on the combustion of the branched-chain alkane 2,2,4-trimethylpentane being set at 100. Branched alkanes like this burn in a more controlled fashion. Draw this molecule.

2,2,4-trimethylpentane

Two processes

Name two processes that could be carried out on a long-chain alkane in order to obtain more branched products.

Alternatives to oil

Oil reserves are finite. What alternatives are there for fuel production?

Various pollutants are produced during combustion of hydrocarbon fuels, namely CO_2, SO_2, NO_x, CO. Complete this table to show the gases and their effects.

Cause	Pollutant gas	Effect
Sulphur present as impurities		
Complete combustion of carbon in the fuel		
Incomplete combustion of fuel		
High temperature and pressure in the petrol engine		

THE JARGON

NO_x is a general formula to show a variety of nitrogen oxides.

Alkenes

Alkenes are unsaturated hydrocarbons whose double bond makes them attractive to electrophiles, causing them to be much more reactive than alkanes.

Bonding in alkenes

Molecular orbitals form when atoms share their electrons.

Draw the shape of s and p atomic orbitals and label them.

Sigma bonds (σ bonds) form when atomic orbitals combine to form molecular orbitals by **end-on-end** overlap.

Show the formation of a sigma bond from the overlap of a p orbital and an s orbital.

This is the type of bond we see in ethane. But in ethene, something different happens. Adjacent p orbitals overlap **sideways** and form pi molecular orbitals (π molecular orbitals).

The shape of an ethene molecule

Draw a molecule of ethene showing all of the σ and π bonds in it.

In one word describe its shape.

Addition reactions of ethene

The table shows addition reactions of ethene as a typical alkene. Complete the products column.

Reactants	Product	Comments
Hydrogen		Ni catalyst at 200 °C
Bromine		Br_2 is decolorized; the test for an alkene
HI		Quick at room temperature
Steam		Catalyst H_3PO_4 at 300 °C and 70 atm
H_2SO_4		Concentrated acid; slow at room temperature
Ethene		LDPE in extreme conditions; HDPE in moderate conditions and with catalyst
$KMnO_4$		Acidified MnO_4^- is decolorized; this is not addition but oxidation

SYLLABUS CHECK
Check your syllabus to see which of these reactions you need and tick them now.

IF YOU HAVE TIME
Practice writing equations for the reactions on your syllabus.

THE JARGON
LDPE is low-density poly(ethene); HDPE is high-density poly(ethene).

Turn the page for some exam questions on this topic ➤

Exam question 1

This question is about propene. Draw displayed formulae and name the products when propene is reacted with the reagents shown.

Reaction with H_2 / Ni.

Steam / H_3PO_4.

Two possible isomers from the reaction with HBr.

Exam question 2

SYLLABUS CHECK
AQA only.

Epoxyethane, a very reactive molecule, is used for making other substances like polyesters and ethane-1,2-diol (antifreeze). Draw a diagram of epoxyethane and explain why it is so reactive.

How is epoxyethane made from ethene?

What are the hazards involved in this process?

Epoxyethane can be reacted to make ethane-1,2-diol. Draw a displayed formula for ethane-1,2-diol.

Epoxyethane can be reacted with alcohols. What are the products used for?

Reaction mechanisms for alkenes

As well as knowing the reactions of alkenes you also need to be able to recall their mechanisms.

SYLLABUS CHECK
Edexcel does not require details of mechanisms at AS.

MECHANISM OF THE REACTION BETWEEN ETHENE AND BROMINE

Consider the mechanism for the reaction between ethene and bromine. As you read through the stages, you need to add various items to the diagram.

Stage 1

The bromine molecule approaches the ethene. The high density of the electrons of the pi bond of ethene causes the bromine to become polarized.

Draw the dipole that will form on bromine.

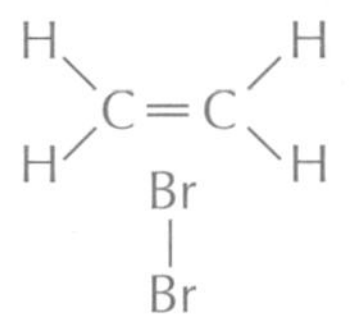

H₂C=CH₂ with Br–Br below

Stage 2

The C=C bond breaks by heterolytic fission. The bromine molecule acts as an electron pair acceptor – an electrophile. At the same time, heterolytic fission of the Br–Br bond occurs and the electron pair moves onto the other bromine atom.

Draw curly arrows to show the movement of electrons out of the double bond onto bromine and the movement of the electron pair out of the Br–Br bond.

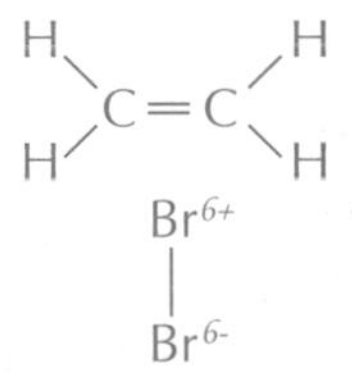

H₂C=CH₂ with $Br^{\delta+}$–$Br^{\delta-}$ below

THE JARGON
A curly arrow shows the movement of a pair of electrons.

Stage 3

An unstable intermediate forms in which one carbon is electron deficient and so carries a positive charge. This is a carbocation, sometimes called a carbonium ion. A bromide ion is in the wings.

Draw the charge onto the carbocation and add a curly arrow to show the movement of the electron pair from the Br^- ion onto the positively charged carbon. Draw the product that forms and name it.

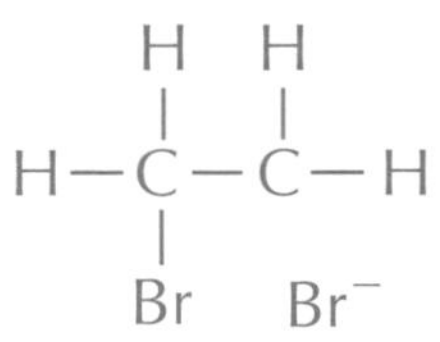

H–C(H)(Br)–C(H)–H with Br^-

How would you classify this reaction?

Turn the page for some exam questions on this topic ➤

SYLLABUS CHECK
All syllabuses say that you should know about the possibility of two isomeric products, but AQA and WJEC specifically want this mechanism.

EXAM QUESTION 1

When propene reacts with hydrogen bromide, there is a possibility of two isomers forming but one is always favoured over the other. By drawing out the mechanism, explain why this is the case. Name both possible products and identify the major product.

Using the molecule printed for you, draw the induced polarity on the HBr molecule and the curly arrow from the C=C bond.

Now work in two columns for the two possibilities. At the top of column 1, add the H atom to the right-hand side of the bond and draw the + on the other carbon. Reverse this in column 2.

Alkyl groups have a positive inductive effect, pushing electrons onto the positively charged carbon. Show any such inductive effects with arrows along the bonds.

Notice that in column 1 there are two alkyl groups pushing electrons onto the carbocation. Label this secondary carbocation.

In column 2 there is only a single alkyl group stabilizing the carbocation. Label this primary carbocation.

Since the secondary carbocation is more stabilized, it is this one that will form the major product. Complete both columns and label the major product.

H–C(H)(H)–C(H)=C(H)(H)

H–Br

EXAM QUESTION 2

Draw the mechanism for the reaction of concentrated sulphuric acid with ethene. Show what happens when water is then added.

SYLLABUS CHECK
AQA only.

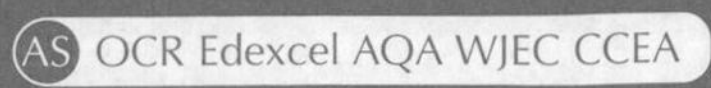

Uses of alkenes

The previous section reviewed some addition reactions of the alkenes. This section places them in an industrial context.

Hydrogenation of vegetable oils

This involves the addition of hydrogen across the double bonds in vegetable oil, causing it to harden and form margarine.

How is this done?

Addition polymerization of ethene

Ethene can be polyermerized to give poly(ethene). Draw two repeat units of this polymer.

Other polymers

By varying the monomer, addition polymerization can produce a whole range of polymers.

For each monomer, draw two repeat units of the polymer and name the polymer.

CH_2CHCl		
CH_3CHCH_2		
CF_2CF_2		

DON'T FORGET
The double bond will not be present in the polymer.

The problem with polymers

Polymer items have replaced many objects that used to be made from natural products. But disposal is a considerable problem for, unlike natural products, most polymers are not biodegradable.

What can we do with polymers once their use is over? Mention any problems associated with the methods you suggest.

Turn the page for some exam questions on this topic ➤

For more on this topic, see pages 147–148 of the *Revision Express A-level Study Guide*

Exam question 1

For each polymer shown, work out its monomer unit, then draw and name it in the monomer column. Name the polymer formed from it. Styrene has been done for you.

Monomer	Polymer	Name
	$\left(\begin{array}{c} CH_3 \\ \vert \\ CH - CH_2 \end{array} \right)_n$	
	$\left(CH_2 - CH_2 \right)_n$	
styrene $C_6H_5CH{=}CH_2$	$\left(\begin{array}{c} C_6H_5 \\ \vert \\ CH - CH_2 \end{array} \right)_n$	poly(styrene)
	$\left(\begin{array}{c} \quad\; Cl \\ \quad\; \vert \\ CH_2 - CH \end{array} \right)_n$	

Exam question 2

Polymers have advantages and disadvantages. One disadvantage is that they are non-biodegradable. What is it about their structure that makes them non-biodegradable?

In order to be reactive, what would the polymer structure need?

Exam question 3

Which of these compounds could undergo addition polymerization? Why could they do this?

What must the monomer unit contain?

- $CH_3CH_2CH_2CH_2CH_2CH_3$ ☐
- $CH_2CH_2CH_2CHCHCH_2CH_2$ ☐
- C_3H_6 ☐
- $CHClCHCl$ ☐
- CH_2ClCH_3 ☐

Alcohols

Alcohols contain the functional group –OH, and they have the general formula $C_nH_{2n-1}OH$

Solubility of alcohols in water

You may have noticed that ethanol and water mix.

Explain why this is the case.

What other physical property of alcohols does this explain?

Making ethanol

SYLLABUS CHECK
Edexcel, WJEC and CCEA don't want you to know about this!

The traditional method is fermentation.

What is needed for fermentation? Write an equation for the reaction of glucose during fermentation.

On p. 57 you saw another method of making ethanol from ethene. What conditions are needed for this?

Reactions of ethanol

Complete this chart. Fill in the structural formula and name the organic product.

SYLLABUS CHECK
For WJEC you only need to know about oxidation of primary alcohols. Other boards vary a lot in their requirements. Use your syllabus to tick off the reactions you need before you start this exercise.

LINKS
This is used as a test for alcohols, as shown on pp. 73–74.

THE JARGON
Refluxing is when a solution is boiled in a flask and the vapours go up into a condenser, cool, condense and drop back into the reaction vessel to react further. XS means excess.

Reacts with	To make	Type of reaction
$NaBr/H_2SO_4$		nucleophilic substitution
Na		reduction
O_2 and ignite		oxidation
PCl_5		nucleophilic substitution
Ethanoic acid and H^+		esterification
Ethanoyl chloride		esterification
XS $Cr_2O_7^{2-}$ and H^+ under reflux		oxidation
$Cr_2O_7^{2-}$ and H^+ distil product as it forms		mild oxidation
Conc. H_2SO_4		dehydration

Turn the page for some exam questions on this topic ➤

For more on this topic, see pages 152–153 of the *Revision Express A-level Study Guide*

EXAM QUESTION 1

SYLLABUS CHECK
Only OCR and CCEA require question 1.

Describe and explain how a sample of ethyl ethanoate may be prepared from ethanol and ethanoic acid in the laboratory.

What reagents are needed?

What type of catalysis is this?

What would you carry out the reaction in?

How is it that the ethyl ethanoate distils off but the reactants remain in the flask?

Write a full equation for the reaction.

In order to purify the distillate, it is shaken with an aqueous solution of sodium carbonate and effervescence is seen. What is the gas likely to be and why is this done?

What reacts with a carbonate?

EXAM QUESTION 2

SYLLABUS CHECK
Check your syllabus to make sure which of these you need.

Fill in the missing organic product or the missing reagents and conditions.

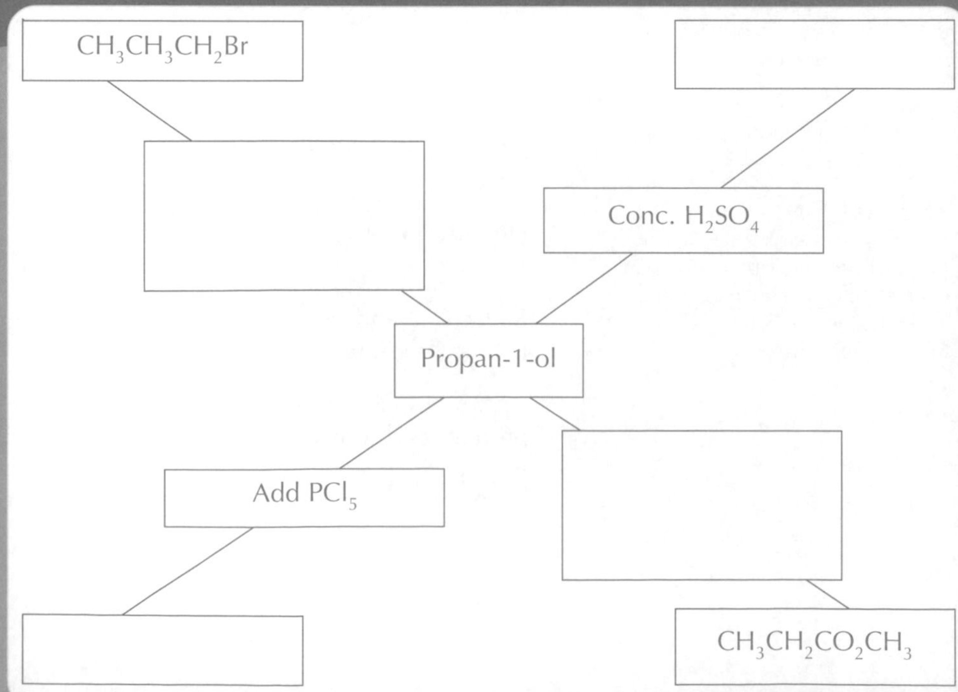

Classification and uses of alcohols

Here we look at the classification of alcohols into primary, secondary and tertiary, and how this affects their behaviour.

Primary, secondary or tertiary?

Label the diagrams to show which is which.

$$CH_3-\underset{\underset{H}{|}}{\overset{\overset{OH}{|}}{C}}-CH_3 \qquad CH_3-\underset{\underset{CH_3}{|}}{\overset{\overset{OH}{|}}{C}}-CH_3 \qquad CH_3-CH_2-OH$$

Oxidation of alcohols

Primary, secondary and tertiary alcohols behave differently during oxidation. Tick the statements that are correct here.

- Mild oxidation of a primary alcohol yields a carboxylic acid ☐
- Refluxing a primary alcohol with excess $H^+/Cr_2O_7^{2-}$ yields a carboxylic acid ☐
- Mild oxidation of a primary alcohol yields a ketone ☐
- Mild oxidation of a primary alcohol yields an aldehyde ☐
- Oxidation of a secondary alcohol yields an aldehyde ☐
- Oxidation of a secondary alcohol yields a ketone ☐
- Oxidation of a secondary alcohol yields first a ketone then a carboxylic acid ☐
- Oxidation of a tertiary alcohol stops at the formation of a ketone ☐
- Oxidation of a tertiary alcohol is not possible under normal conditions ☐

LINKS
These tests can be used in the identification of alcohols, as shown on pp. 73–74.

In order to identify the class an alcohol belongs to, first it is oxidized and then the oxidation product is identified.

Using [O] to signify an oxidizing agent, write equations for the mild and complete oxidation of propan-1-ol. Name the products formed.

Mild oxidation

Strong oxidation

SYLLABUS CHECK
Only WJEC and CCEA need this at AS.

Reduction of aldehydes

The aldehydes formed by oxidation of primary alcohols can themselves be reduced.

What reagent could you use?

Write an equation for the reduction of propanal, using [H] to signify the reducing agent.

Turn the page for some exam questions on this topic ➤

SYLLABUS CHECK
AQA only.

EXAM QUESTION 1

Alcohols can undergo nucleophilic substitution reactions. Draw the structure of ethanol and indicate on your formula where it would be attractive to nucleophiles.

Draw the displayed formula for ethanol.

Nucleophiles are attracted to positive centres in the molecule. Label the bond polarity on the OH group.

The presence of H^+ catalyses many reactions of alcohols. How does the presence of H^+ help the reaction?

Draw another ethanol molecule and label the bond polarity of the OH bond.

There is only one place an H^+ ion will be attracted. Use : for a lone pair and a curly arrow to show what will happen.

What stable group could now leave the molecule?

During nucleophilic substitution, one group in the molecule leaves and is replaced by another. Which is the best leaving group, H_2O or OH^-?

What type of catalysis is this?

EXAM QUESTION 2

SYLLABUS CHECK
AQA only.

The reaction of alcohols with concentrated sulphuric acid is used to make alkenes. Draw a reaction mechanism for this, using ethanol as an example. Show the part that H^+ ions play.

Draw a molecule of ethanol and mark on the bond polarity and relevant lone pairs.

Think about the role of the H^+ ion.

Draw curly arrows.

SYLLABUS CHECK
All boards could reasonably ask this.

EXAM QUESTION 3

Give uses for two named alcohols.

Halogenoalkanes

The halogenoalkanes have the general formula $C_nH_{2n+1}X$ where X is Cl, Br or I. We have seen how they can be made from alkenes and alcohols and now we see how they react.

Properties of halogenoalkanes

Draw a displayed formula for chloroethane and label the bond polarity.

Can it hydrogen bond with water? Check to see if it has H directly bonded to N, O, F. Does it have a permanent dipole?

Look at the data below and compare the boiling temperature of chloroethane with the boiling temperatures of propan-1-ol and butane.

Name	T_B (°C)	M_r
propan-1-ol	97.5	60.1
chloroethane	12.5	64.5
butane	–0.4	58.1

Would you expect chloroethane to be miscible with water?

THE JARGON
Miscible means that it will mix.

Substitution reactions of halogenoalkanes

Look again at your diagram of chloroethane then read through these statements and tick any row that has a correct observation and deduction.

Observation	Deduction	
The carbon adjacent to Cl has a partial positive charge	It will be attractive to electrophiles	
The carbon adjacent to Cl has a partial positive charge	It will be attractive to nucleophiles.	
If sodium hydroxide is reacted with it, the OH^- ion can act as an electron donor	It is an electrophile	
If sodium hydroxide is reacted with it, the OH^- ion can act as an electron donor	It is a nucleophile	

SYLLABUS CHECK
Check your syllabus now to see which reactions it mentions. There is much variation between syllabuses.

When halogenoalkanes are heated under reflux with aqueous NaOH, a substitution reaction occurs. The halogenoalkane is hydrolysed.

Write an equation to show the reaction of chloroethane and aqueous NaOH.

When refluxed with ethanolic NaOH, an elimination reaction occurs.

Write an equation for the reaction.

Another nucleophilic substitution occurs when chloroethane reacts with concentrated ammonia in ethanol.

How can ammonia act as a nucleophile and what will be the product of this reaction?

Turn the page for some exam questions on this topic ➤

For more on this topic, see page 150 of the *Revision Express A-level Study Guide*

SYLLABUS CHECK
This question is for everyone.

EXAM QUESTION 1

5.00 cm^3 of 1-iodobutane were refluxed with an excess of NaOH and 2.10 g of the product butan-1-ol were collected. What was the percentage yield of this reaction? (M_r iodobutane = 184.0, M_r butanol = 74.1, density iodobutane = 1.62 g cm^{-3})

$CH_3CH_2CH_2CH_2I + OH^- \rightarrow CH_3CH_2CH_2CH_2OH + I^-$

density = mass / volume

Calculate the mass of iodobutane used.

Calculate moles of iodobutane.

How many moles of product will it give?

Calculate the maximum yield of butanol.

SYLLABUS CHECK
This question is for AQA and Edexcel only. Edexcel does not require you to know how to convert a nitrile to a carboxylic acid.

THE JARGON
A nitrile has the functional group –C≡N.

EXAM QUESTION 2

The reaction of bromoethane with cyanide ions can be used to extend the length of the carbon chain in a molecule. Describe how this reaction should be carried out and show how the product is converted to a carboxylic acid.

State the reaction conditions and the product.

Write an equation for the reaction of bromoethane with CN^- ions.

Explain how is the nitrile converted to a carboxylic acid.

Write an equation for the reaction of propanenitrile with dilute sulphuric acid.

You might finally want to convert this to propanol. What type of reagent would you use to convert a carboxylic acid to an alcohol?

Reaction mechanisms of halogenoalkanes

We look at the nucleophilic substitution of halogenoalkanes and how it relates to rate of hydrolysis. We also look at elimination.

SYLLABUS CHECK
Edexcel does not require *any* mechanisms, so go straight to exam question 2 on page 70.

SYLLABUS CHECK
AQA, OCR and CCEA only.

Nucleophilic substitution of primary halogenoalkanes

This substitution is a one-step reaction that occurs in aqueous conditions. Follow the steps to show how it works.

Draw a diagram of bromoethane and label the partial charges. Draw the attacking OH^- ion with its lone pair.

Draw two curly arrows to show the one-step substitution. Show the products.

Elimination of hydrogen bromide from bromoethane

SYLLABUS CHECK
AQA and OCR only.

If the reaction between bromoethane and NaOH is carried out in anhydrous conditions in ethanolic solution, there is a very different result.

What product will form? How is the OH^- ion acting here?

Add curly arrows to show how bromoethane reacts with OH^- to release a molecule of water and a Br^- ion. Draw the products.

```
   H  H
   |  |
H—C—C—Br
   |  |
   H  H
```

THE JARGON
A tertiary halogenoalkane is where there are three methyl groups attached to the carbon atom adjacent to the halogen.

Elimination is more likely than substitution in tertiary halogenoalkanes.

Draw the simplest possible tertiary bromoalkane and name it.

SYLLABUS CHECK
AQA only.

Tick the reasons why you think tertiary halogenoalkanes are more likely to undergo elimination than primary halogenoalkanes.

- Alkyl groups push electrons onto the carbon adjacent to the halogen ☐
- Alkyl groups make the partial charge on the carbon more positive ☐
- Alkyl groups make the partial charge on the carbon less positive ☐
- The alkyl groups are bulky and get in the way of the attacking OH^- nucleophile ☐
- The OH^- can only get near the outer hydrogens, so it acts as a base and pulls a hydrogen off ☐
- The effect of alkyl groups is to make the carbon attached to the halogen less attractive to nucleophiles ☐

Turn the page for some exam questions on this topic ➤

Exam question 1

SYLLABUS CHECK
OCR and CCEA only.

Explain how and why the rate of hydrolysis of halogenoalkanes varies with the particular halogen present and explain how you could demonstrate this.

How does the rate of hydrolysis vary? Add a label to the arrow on this diagram.

—C—Cl —C—Br —C—I
→

Why does the halogen make a difference?

How would you demonstrate this? Number this sequence of steps to show how.

- Add 2 cm^3 of ethanol to act as a solvent ☐
- Warm the tubes in a water bath to 50 °C ☐
- Precipitates of silver halides will form ☐
- Place 2 cm^3 of silver nitrate solution in each of three tubes ☐
- When up to 50 °C, add 0.5 cm^3 of 1-chlorobutane to tube A, 0.5 cm^3 of 1-bromobutane to tube B and 0.5 cm^3 of 1-iodobutane to tube C ☐
- Precipitation will occur most rapidly in tube C, then tube B and finally tube A ☐
- Replace in the water bath and observe ☐

Exam question 2

SYLLABUS CHECK
All boards.

When 2-bromo-3-methylbutane reacts with NaOH under various conditions, a variety of products are possible. Complete this chart to show the possibilities. Draw formulae for the products.

Could more than one product form if OH^- acts as a base?

OH^- acts as	Reaction type	Product
Base		$H_2C{=}CH{-}CH(CH_3){-}CH_3$
	elimination	
Nucleophile		

Uses of halogenoalkanes

Fluorohalogenoalkanes and fluoroalkanes have many uses but there are pitfalls too.

Chlorofluorocarbons (CFCs)

Draw a displayed formula for 1,1,1-trichloroethane.

1,1,1-trichloroethane

This substance was once used as the thinner for Tippex and other liquid paper products. Why is its use a problem?

How is it that such compounds can reach the upper atmosphere without reacting with anything on the way?

How do the C–Cl bonds break when they reach the upper atmosphere?

What happens to the bond there, and why is this a problem?

Uses of CFCs

Say whether the following statements are true of false; explain what is wrong with the statements that are false.

Statement	
If your fridge contains CFCs then care should be taken when disposing of it	
CFCs have been used as the blowing agent in making polystyrene foams	
Chloroethane can be used to make the polymer PVC	
Halogenoalkanes make very useful intermediates in organic synthesis because the halogen can be readily replaced by nucleophilic addition	
Tetrafluoroethene is used to make the polymer PTFE	
Even if we stopped using CFCs immediately, it would be a long time before ozone depletion abated because the free radicals they produce are not used up during reactions	
CFCs replaced butane as a propellant in aerosols; now butane has come back into use despite its obvious hazards	
CFCs are used in degreasing and dry-cleaning; covalent bonding makes them good solvents for organic compounds	

Turn the page for some exam questions on this topic ➤

For more on this topic, see page 151 of the *Revision Express A-level Study Guide*

To help you this time, the steps have been given in the right order but the right-hand column is for you to write the equations. Use the text to help you.

Exam question 1

Chloroflurocarbons (CFCs) are now known to cause depletion of the ozone layer that protects us from harmful UV radiation. Using CCl_2F_2 as an example, outline this process, explaining the way in which the action is catalytic.

THE JARGON

Free radicals have an unpaired electron, which makes them very reactive. The chlorine free radical may be written as Cl· or just Cl.

CFCs drift up to the upper atmosphere where they absorb energy, breaking the C–Cl bond in the molecule and forming Cl· radicals	
The chlorine free radicals react with ozone and form ClO· radicals	
The ClO· radical reacts with oxygen radicals present in the upper atmosphere, making oxygen gas and restoring Cl· free radicals	
The overall reaction is removal of ozone	

DON'T FORGET

You get this by adding together the equations for the second and third steps in the process.

Exam question 2

How many grams of each element would there be in 100 g?

Analysis of a halogenoalkane shows it to contain 17.8% C, 52.6% Cl, 1.5% H and 28.1% F. Calculate its empirical formula, and given that it has M_r = 135, obtain its molecular formula. Draw its four isomers. Use C = 12, Cl = 35.5, F = 19, H = 1.

How many moles of each?

What is the simplest ratio?

What is the empirical formula?

1,1-dichloro-2,2-difluoroethane

1,2dichloro-1,1-difluoroethane

1,2-dichloro-1,2-difluoroethane

1,1-dichloro-1,2-difluoroethane

Organic analysis

You will meet these tests in your practical work but they also appear in theory papers.

WHAT ARE THE TESTS?

For each of the tests and observations here, say what functional group is present

Test	Observation	Functional group present
Add bromine water and shake	Bromine decolorizes	
Addition of H^+/MnO_4^-	Purple colour decolorized	
Add PCl_5	Steamy fumes (of HCl)	
Warm with acidified $Cr_2O_7^{2-}$	Solution turns from orange to brown to green	
Add Tollen's reagent and warm	A silver layer is deposited on the sides of the tube	
Add Fehling's solution and warm	Brick red precipitate	
Hydrolysis by base followed by addition of $HNO_3/AgNO_3$	Formation of white, cream or yellow precipitate	
Add sodium carbonate solution	Effervescence (CO_2 forms)	

THE JARGON

Tollen's reagent is silver nitrate dissolved in ammonia solution. Fehling's is an alkaline solution of Cu^{2+} ions.

USING INFRARED SPECTROSCOPY

Spectrum of ethanol

Label the O–H peak and the C–O peak.

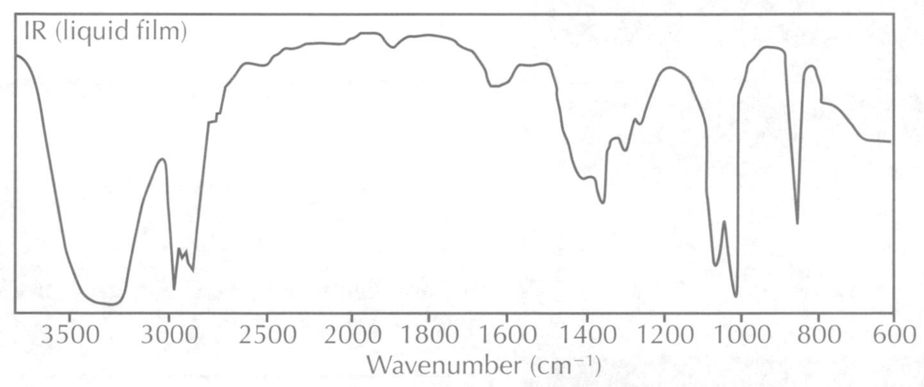

SYLLABUS CHECK

OCR requires you to interpret infrared spectroscopy data, but you do not need to how the technique works.

Spectrum of butan-2-one

Label the C=O peak. Remember that butan-2-one is a ketone.

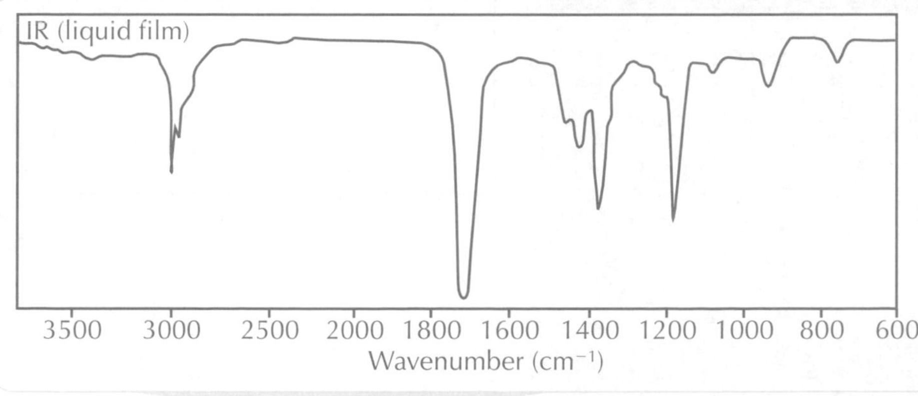

DON'T FORGET

	Wavenumber (cm^{-1})
C–O in alcohols	1000–300
C=O in ketones and carboxylic acids	1680–750
O–H in alcohols	3230–3550
O–H in carboxylic acids	2500–3300 broad

Turn the page for some exam questions on this topic ➤

Exam question 1

LINKS
Check p. 52 to remind yourself what is meant by structural isomerism and *cis / trans* isomerism.

A, which has $M_r = 74$, is tested with PCl_5 and found to release steamy fumes of B. When A is treated with concentrated sulphuric acid, it produces two different structural isomers, C and D. When A is oxidized using $H^+/Cr_2O_7^{2-}$ the colour of the solution turns from orange to green but the product formed, E, does not give a positive test with Tollen's reagent. Name each of A to E and write balanced equations for all reactions.

From the PCl_5 test and M_r, what can you say about A? What is B?

Write an equation for this reaction.

Write an equation for the dehydration of A. Draw the displayed formulae and name the two structural isomers, C and D, that form.

Could A be butan-1-ol? If not, what is it?

On oxidation does an aldehyde form? If not, what has?

Write an equation for this oxidation and name the product.

SYLLABUS CHECK
Question 2(a) for OCR only.

Exam question 2

Label any significant peaks in this spectrum and use them to identify the functional groups present.

You only need to think about whether it has O–H, C=O or C–O. Assume no other functional groups are present.

SYLLABUS CHECK
The rest of the question is for any board.

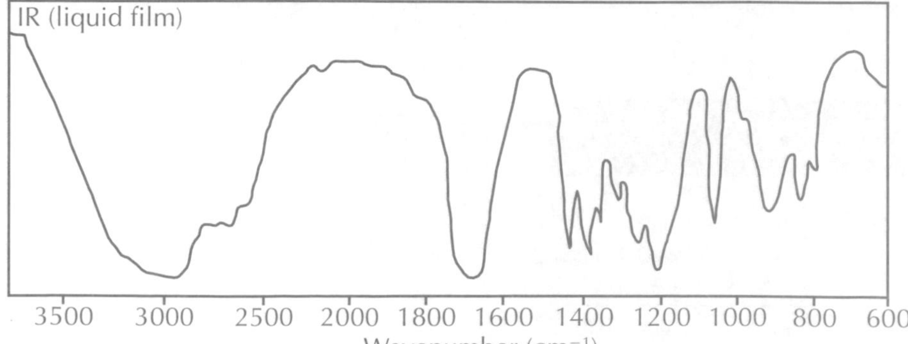

Answer section

Answer section

SEE HOW YOU GOT ON BY CHECKING AGAINST THE ANSWERS GIVEN HERE.

Have you remembered to fill in the self-check circles? Do this to track your progress.

For more detail on the topics covered in this book, you can check the *Revision Express A-level Study Guide*, your class notes or your own textbook. You can also find exam questions and model answers at www.revision-express.com.

Don't forget, tear out these answers and put them in your folder for handy revision reference!

AS OCR Edexcel AQA WJEC CCEA

Atoms and atomic mass

Atoms are unbelievably small and have equally small masses. Since these small numbers are hard to work with, a relative scale of masses is used, where everything is compared to the mass of an atom of carbon-12, which is assigned a mass of 12.

Some definitions

Define each of these terms. The first one has been done for you.

THE JARGON
A weighted average takes into account that isotopes are not present in equal amounts.

A_r, relative atomic mass	Weighted average mass of an atom compared to one-twelfth the mass of a ^{12}C atom
M_r, relative molecular mass	Weighted average mass of a molecule compared to one-twelfth the mass of a ^{12}C atom
Isotopic mass	Mass of a particular isotope compared to one-twelfth the mass of a ^{12}C atom
Formula mass	Weighted average mass of a formula unit compared to one-twelfth the mass of a ^{12}C atom

Basics of mass spectroscopy

Relative masses are measured using a mass spectrometer. These five statements outline its principles.

Number the boxes to show the order in which the stages occur.

- [3] The positive ions are accelerated using a high voltage and deflected by a magnetic field
- [2] An outer electron is knocked off the atom or molecule using an electron gun. Positive ions are formed
- [4] Ions of low mass are deflected more than heavier ions
- [1] The substance is turned to a gas and bombarded with electrons
- [5] Ions are detected and a mass spectrum is produced

Calculating relative atomic mass from isotopic data

If a sample of an element is examined, there will be different peaks in the spectrum due to the different isotopes it contains. If a sample of lithium is examined, two peaks are seen. The heights of the peaks can be measured to find the percentage of each isotope present.

Here is some data for lithium: 7.42% is ^{6}Li and 92.58% is ^{7}Li.

Use the data provided to calculate the relative atomic mass of lithium.

The weighted average is given by

$(7.42/100 \times 6) + (92.58/100 \times 7)$

$= 6.93$

Turn the page for some exam questions on this topic ➤

For more on this topic, see pages 8–9 of the *Revision Express A-level Study Guide*

Exam question 1

Here is a simplified mass spectrum for lead. The height of each peak is proportional to the percentage of that isotope present. Using this spectrum, calculate the relative atomic mass of lead.

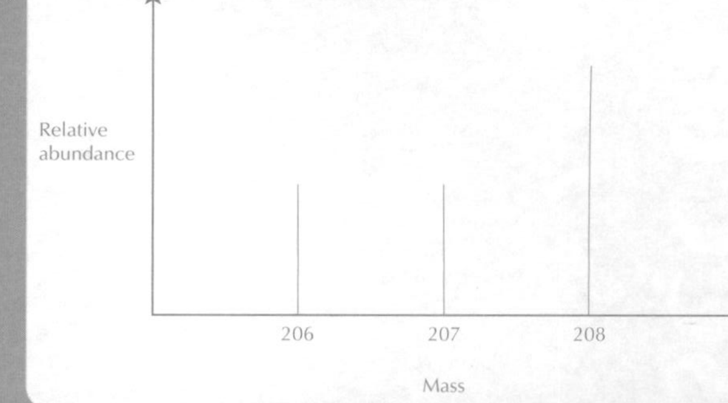

How many isotopes are present?
Three isotopes are present

Measure the relative peak heights and add them together. What value do you get?
Total peak height is 1 + 1 + 2 = **4**

What fraction of each isotope is present?
Fraction of ^{206}Pb = 1/4; ^{207}Pb = 1/4; ^{208}Pb = 1/2

Find the weighted average of the isotopes.
$(1/4 \times 206) + (1/4 \times 207) + (1/2 \times 208) = 207.25$

Exam question 2

Give two uses of mass spectroscopy.

Finding relative atomic masses of elements
Identifying the presence of particular elements,
e.g. the Mars probe carried a mass spectrometer
Identifying particular molecules
Determining structures of molecules

SYLLABUS CHECK
Only WJEC will require you to interpret data for simple organic molecules.

DON'T FORGET
The covalent bond may be broken during ionization. Show the charge on the ion.

Exam question 3

The mass spectrum of chlorine, Cl_2, has peaks at 35, 37 and 70. Interpret these peaks and predict which other two peaks should also be present.

The peak at 35 is from $^{35}Cl^+$
The peak at 37 is from $^{37}Cl^+$
The peak at 70 is from $^{35}Cl_2^+$

There should also be peaks at 72 from $^{35}Cl^{37}Cl^+$ and at 74, from $^{37}Cl_2^+$.

AS OCR Edexcel AQA WJEC CCEA

Calculations in chemistry

Calculations can involve reacting masses, volumes of gases or concentrations of solutions. They involve the idea of a mole.

WHAT IS A MOLE?

Explain what you understand by a mole. In your definition you should refer to isotope carbon-12 and Avogadro's number.

A mole is the amount of a substance that contains the same number of atoms as 12 g of the isotope carbon-12. This number of particles is known as Avogadro's number. It has the value 6.02×10^{23}.

Work out the molar mass (mass of 1 mole) for the substances given in the table. Show your working.

Cl_2	$2 \times 35.5 = 71.0$ g
CaO	$40.1 + 16.0 = 56.1$ g
$MgCl_2$	$24.3 + (2 \times 35.5) = 95.3$ g
$Fe(OH)_2$	$55.8 + 2(16.0 + 1.0) = 89.8$ g
H_2SO_4	$(2 \times 1.0) + 32.1 + (4 \times 16.0) = 98.1$ g

DON'T FORGET
To find the number of moles, you divide the mass (in grams) by the mass of 1 mole, $n = m / M_r$.

When gases are involved, what do you need to remember?

Draw lines to link a statement in the first column with one in the second.

1 $1\ m^3 =$	m^3	3
2 1 mole of any gas at RTP occupies	1 000 000 cm^3	1
3 In $pV = nRT$, V must be given in	24 dm^3	2
4 1 mole of any gas at STP occupies	Pa	5
5 In $pV = nRT$, p must be given in	1000 cm^3	6
6 $1\ dm^3 =$	22.4 dm^3	4

SYLLABUS CHECK
The formula $pV = nRT$ is only in the AQA and WJEC syllabuses.

For solutions

When solutions are involved, you need to use the formula $n = cv$. In this equation, what do the symbols represent and what are their units?

Symbol	Quantity	Unit
n	amount	mol
c	concentration	mol dm^{-3}
v	volume	dm^3

Some terminology

What do you understand by the terms 'empirical formula' and 'molecular formula'?

Empirical formula
Simplest whole number ratio of atoms present, e.g. CH_3

Molecular formula
Actual number of atoms present, e.g. C_2H_6

Turn the page for some exam questions on this topic ➤

For more on this topic, see pages 10–11 of the *Revision Express A-level Study Guide*

EXAM QUESTION 1

When 4.86 g of magnesium undergo complete combustion in oxygen they form 8.06 g of oxide. Calculate the empirical formula of the oxide and then find the volume of oxygen reacted at RTP.

DON'T FORGET
When doing calculations, find the number of moles, then find the ratios, then work out the answer.

Write symbols	Mg	O
Put in mass	4.86 g	3.20 g
Find moles	4.86/24.3	3.20/16.0
	0.200 mol	0.200 mol
Simplest ratio	1	1
Formula	MgO	

Write a balanced equation for the combustion of magnesium. Include state symbols.

$2Mg_{(s)} + O_{2(g)} \rightarrow 2MgO_{(s)}$ (equation 1)

Moles of Mg = 0.200

From equation (1), 2 mol Mg react with 1 mol O_2, so 0.200 mol Mg reacts with 0.100 mol O_2

Calculate the volume of oxygen that is reacted (at RTP).

1 mol O_2 occupies 24 dm^3 at RTP, so 0.100 mol will occupy **2.4 dm^3**

The magnesium oxide then reacts with 0.50 mol dm^{-3} HCl. What volume of this acid will be needed to make it react completely?

Write an equation for the reaction of MgO with HCl.

$MgO_{(s)} + 2HCl_{(aq)} \rightarrow MgCl_{2(aq)} + H_2O_{(l)}$ (equation 2)

Find moles.

From equation (1), we know that 2 mol Mg make 2 mol MgO, so 0.200 mol MgO will form

Refer to the equation for ratios.

From equation (2), we can see that 1 mol MgO reacts with 2 mol HCl, so 0.200 mol MgO needs 0.400 mol HCl

Find the answer.

Use $n = cv$

Rearrange to give $v = n / c$

Substitute the values:
$v = 0.400$ mol / 0.50 mol dm^{-3}

So $v = 0.80\ dm^3$ or **800 cm^3 HCl**

Atomic structure

AS OCR Edexcel AQA WJEC CCEA

Atoms are the building blocks of chemistry and you need to know about the structure of an atom.

Structure of the atom

Here are the properties of the three subatomic particles.

Complete this table to show their properties.

	Relative charge	Relative mass	Where found
protons	+1	1	nucleus
neutrons	0	1	nucleus
electrons	−1	1/1 840	orbiting

Each different element is represented by a symbol. For example, the symbol for potassium is K and it may be shown like this:

mass number
atomic number $^{39}_{19}K$

What does the proton number tell us?

The proton number, or atomic number, tells us how many protons an atom has. Atoms are always neutral, so the number of protons equals the number of electrons in an atom.

What does the mass number tell us?

The mass number tells us how many protons *plus* neutrons an atom has.

Complete this chart to show how many protons, neutrons and electrons there are in each atom or ion. $^{39}_{19}K$ and $^{40}_{19}K$ are isotopes.

Atom / ion	Protons	Neutrons	Electrons
$^{39}_{19}K$	19	20	19
$^{40}_{19}K$	19	21	19
$^{39}_{19}K^+$	19	20	18

Explain what an isotope is.

Isotopes have the same number of protons but different mass numbers. This is because they have different numbers of neutrons. Their chemical behaviour is identical.

DON'T FORGET
You should be able to show the electron arrangement of the atoms up to Z = 36 using spdf notation.

Show the electron arrangement for K.

$^{39}_{19}K$ has the arrangement $1s^22s^22p^63s^23p^64s^1$. (Remember the 4s orbitals fill before the 3d).

Define, using equations, what is meant by first and second ionization energies. Ionization energy is the energy required to remove one mole of electrons.

First ionization energy: $M_{(g)} \rightarrow M^+_{(g)} + e^-$

Second ionization energy: $M^+_{(g)} \rightarrow M^{2+}_{(g)} + e^-$

Turn the page for some exam questions on this topic ➤

For more on this topic, see pages 12–13 of the *Revision Express A-level Study Guide*

Exam question 1

Give the spdf notation for Se, which has a proton number of 34.

Se has $1s^22s^22p^63s^23p^63d^{10}4s^24p^4$

Give the spdf notation for Mn^{2+}, which has a proton number of 25.

DON'T FORGET
Transition metals always lose their outer s electrons before they lose their d electrons.

Mn^{2+} has $1s^22s^22p^63s^23p^63d^5$

Draw a diagram to show the electronic configuration of oxygen, atomic number 8, using an 'electrons in boxes' notation.

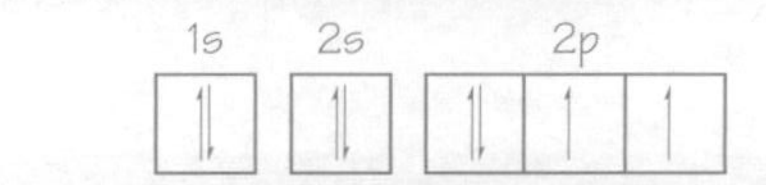

Complete the energy level diagram for Al to show how electrons fill the energy levels.

DON'T FORGET
The order of filling orbitals is shown on this diagram.

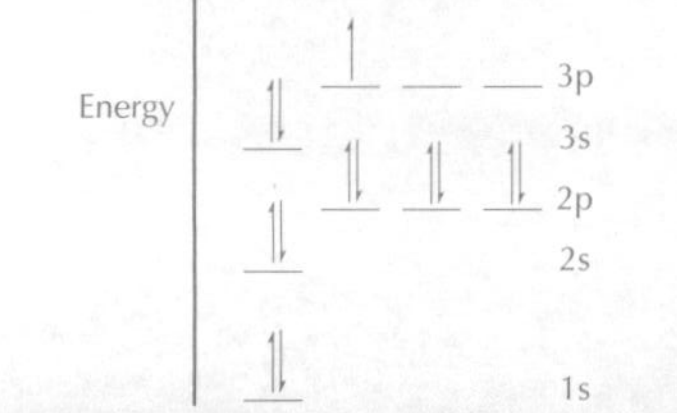

Exam question 2

**The successive ionization energies of an element vary like this.
To which group of the periodic table does the element belong? Explain your reasoning.**

LINKS
For a more detailed discussion of trends in ionization energy, see pp. 37–38.

Look for a big jump from row to row.

Number of the ionization energy	Ionization energy (kJ mol^{-1})
1	1 060
2	1 900
3	2 920
4	4 960
5	6 280
6	21 200
7	25 900
8	30 500

DON'T FORGET
The factors that affect ionization energy are nuclear charge, electron shielding and the distance of the outer electron from the nucleus.

There is a steady increase in energy needed to remove successive electrons, as the effective nuclear charge on the remaining electrons increases. After the fifth electron is removed, there is a very big jump. The sixth electron is taken from an inner shell of electrons, so it is in group 5.

AS OCR Edexcel AQA WJEC CCEA

Ionic bonding

Ionic bonding is the electrostatic attraction between two oppositely charged ions and occurs when atoms with large differences in electronegativity combine.

THE JARGON
Electronegativity is the ability of an atom to attract the bonding electrons towards it.

When does ionic bonding occur? ○○○

Here are some statements about electronegativity.

Tick the statements that are true.

- It increases as you go across periods ☑
- It increases as you go down groups ☐
- A metal and a non-metal will generally have a large difference in electronegativity ☑

Draw a ring round the compounds from this list that you would expect to be ionic.

(Li_2O) CH_4 CO_2 (NaCl) NH_3 (MgO) H_2O

The electron arrangement of Li is $1s^22s^1$ and that of oxygen is $1s^22s^22p^4$. What does each of these atoms need to do in order to have a full outer shell of electrons like their nearest noble gases?

Lithium loses 1 electron and becomes a Li^+ ion.
Oxygen gains 2 electrons and becomes an O^{2-} ion.

What will these oppositely charged ions do?

The oppositely charged ions attract each other.
This electrostatic attraction is an ionic bond.

Drawing diagrams of ionic bonding ○○○

This loss and gain of electrons can be shown using dot and cross diagrams. For simplicity, only the outer shell electrons are shown.

Here is such a diagram for Li_2O.

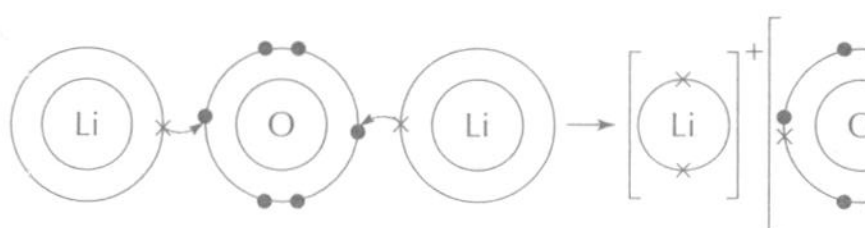

Draw dot and cross diagrams for MgO and label the ions that form.

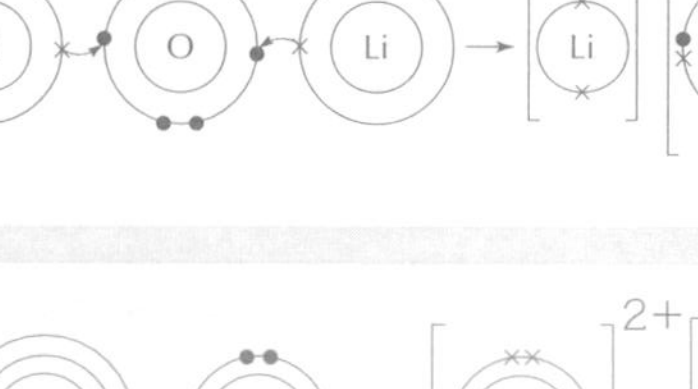

What sort of structure do the oppositely charged ions form?

They form a giant ionic lattice.

THE JARGON
A lattice is some sort of regular and ordered arrangement of particles held together by some sort of force.

Turn the page for some exam questions on this topic ➤

For more on this topic, see pages 14–19 of the *Revision Express A-level Study Guide*

Exam question 1 ●●●

DON'T FORGET
When asked to show bonding, always check whether you should draw a diagram for ionic or covalent bonding. In this case there is clearly a metal and a non-metal.

(a) Draw a dot and cross diagram to show how the bonding in sodium chloride occurs.

The bonding is ionic, so the diagram shows electrons being lost by Na and gained by Cl.

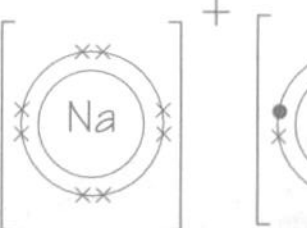
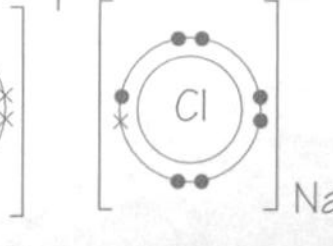

DON'T FORGET
If you think ionic, then think giant ionic lattice.

WATCH OUT
When you draw the structure, take care to avoid using solid lines between the ions as these are used to represent covalent bonds.

(b) Draw a diagram to show a sodium chloride lattice.

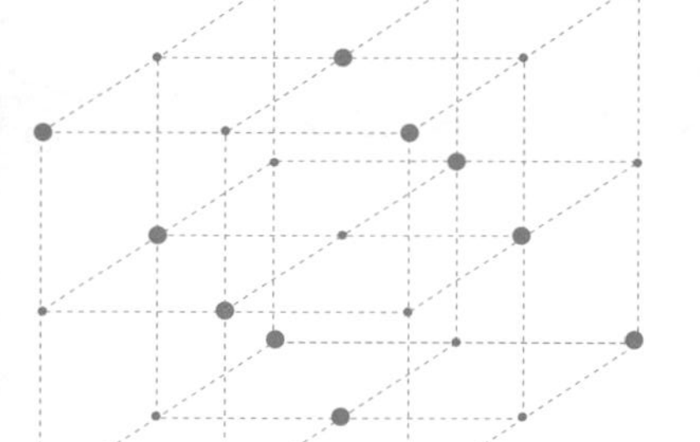

(c) Describe what properties you would expect sodium chloride to have; relate these properties to its structure.

Ask yourself how easy it will be to break down the structure and what will happen when it does break down.

In the lattice each Na^+ ion is surrounded by six oppositely charged Cl^- ions, and each Cl^- ion by six Na^+ ions. The strong electrostatic attraction between these ions means melting temperature and boiling temperature are fairly high.

When molten or dissolved in water, ions are free to move, so dissolved NaCl will conduct electricity.

The lattice can be broken down by water, which is a polar solvent. The polar water molecules surround the ions in the lattice and overcome the forces holding the ions in place.

LINKS
To find out why water is such a good solvent, see pp. 17–18.

(d) How would you expect the melting point of magnesium oxide to compare with that of sodium chloride?

It is the attraction of the ions that determines the melting point. Think about the ionic attractions in MgO and NaCl.

The ions in magnesium oxide are more highly charged and will attract each other more strongly, so you would expect MgO to have a higher melting temperature than NaCl.

AS OCR Edexcel AQA WJEC CCEA

Covalent bonding

When the difference in electronegativity between two atoms is small (generally between two non-metals), the atoms must share their electrons in order to gain full outer shells. These atoms bond covalently.

What is a covalent bond?

When a pair of electrons is shared between atoms, there is a force of attraction between the nuclei of each atom and the shared pair of electrons. This is a covalent bond. A single bond is shown as a single 'stick' joining the two atoms, e.g. H–Br.

How do we draw covalent bonds?

The sharing of electrons can be shown using dot and cross diagrams.

Draw dot and cross diagrams and stick diagrams for the following molecules: H_2, HCl, H_2O, CO_2. The first one has been done for you.

H–H

H–Cl

H–O–H

O=C=O

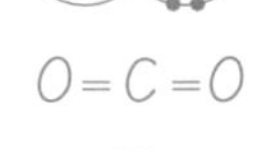

DON'T FORGET
It is easiest to show the outer electrons only. You can use circles to show the inner shells but there's no need.

THE JARGON
The pairs of electrons not involved in bonding are called lone pairs.

Dative covalent bonds (coordinate bonds)

These occur when both electrons of the covalent bond originate from one of the atoms. They behave just like covalent bonds and they are shown as an arrow in stick diagrams.

Draw a dot and cross diagram to show the covalent bonding in $AlCl_3$. Note that Al only has six electrons around it, not eight. In order to obtain electrons in its outside shell, $AlCl_3$ dimerizes. Draw a stick diagram to show how this dimer forms.

Cl ˣ• Al ˣ• Cl
ˣ•
Cl

$AlCl_3$

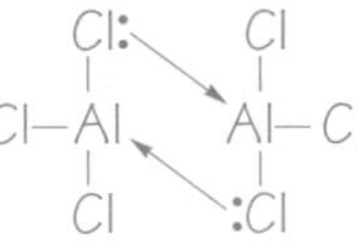

Al_2Cl_6

DON'T FORGET
You will need arrows.

A sliding scale between ionic and covalent

Ionic bonding occurs when electronegativity differences are large and covalent bonding occurs when they are small. In between there is a sliding scale, and if the difference is moderate then we may get an ionic substance with a degree of covalent character.

Rewrite this list in order of increasing ionic character.

CsF CH_4 F_2 HF $AlCl_3$ NaCl

F_2 CH_4 HF $AlCl_3$ NaCl CsF

increasing ionic character →

LINKS
To remind yourself about electronegativity, see p. 11.

Turn the page for some exam questions on this topic ➤

For more on this topic, see pages 14–16 of the *Revision Express A-level Study Guide*

Exam question 1

Would you expect the following compounds to be covalent or ionic?

potassium sulphide	ionic
hydrogen sulphide	covalent
sodium hydride	ionic
carbon dioxide	covalent

Exam question 2

Hints are given below but try to do the question without them first.

(a) Draw both dot and cross diagrams and stick diagrams to show the bonding in C_2H_4 (ethene) and NH_3 (ammonia).

ethene

ammonia

H–N–H
|
H

DON'T FORGET
Ethene contains a double bond. Ammonia has a lone pair.

(b) Draw both dot and cross diagrams and stick diagrams to show the bonding in an ammonium ion.

ammonium ion

DON'T FORGET
You must show all the outer electrons, not just the bonding electrons. You will need to draw an arrow on the stick diagram.

(c) Draw a diagram to show how the iodine molecules are arranged in a crystal of iodine.

•—• = I_2

SYLLABUS CHECK
Only AQA and WJEC need a drawing to show the structure of iodine.

(d) Explain why the members of group 7, the halogens, are all volatile and why the boiling temperature increases down the group.

There are only weak forces holding the individual molecules together. These are caused by temporary dipoles that are set up as the molecules become close to each other. Known as van der Waals forces, they are on average about 100 times weaker than a covalent bond. The size of these temporary dipoles increases as the number of electrons in a molecule increases, so as you go down group 7, the boiling temperatures increase. This is evident in that Cl_2 and F_2 are gases, Br_2 is a liquid and I_2 is a solid.

WATCH OUT
Never just say that the halogens are volatile because they are covalently bonded. Covalent bonds are strong. What is it that holds one molecule to another?

Shapes of molecules and ions

When atoms combine to form molecules, we can work out the shape by using the electron pair repulsion theory.

Complete the last two columns of this table to remind yourself about the shapes of molecules. Show the bond angle on your diagrams.

SYLLABUS CHECK
Only Edexcel and AQA include negative ions.

Rules for working out the shape of molecules

Pairs of electrons	Based on the shape	Lone pairs	Shape	Diagram
2	linear	0	linear	
3	trigonal	0	trigonal	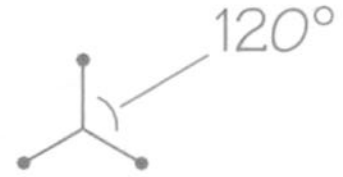 120°
3	trigonal	1	non-linear	 120°
4	tetrahedral	0	tetrahedral	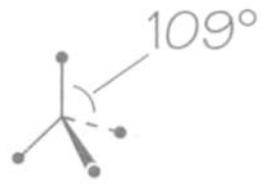 109°
4	tetrahedral	1	pyramidal	 107°
4	tetrahedral	2	non-linear	 105°
6	octahedral	0	octahedral	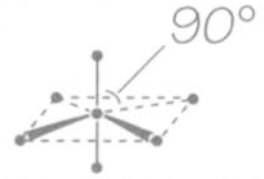 90°
6	octahedral	2	square planar	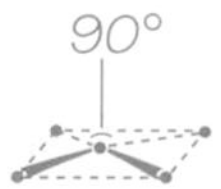 90°

Try this out for a water molecule

In water there are four pairs of electrons around the central oxygen atom, so it is based on a tetrahedral shape, but since two of these are lone pairs, the shape must be non-linear.

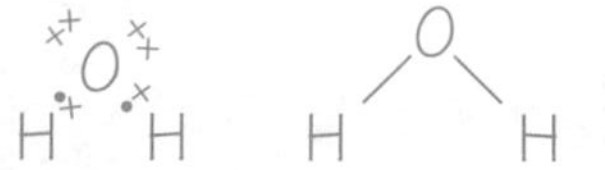

The bond angle in water is about 105°. Why is it less than 109°, the tetrahedral angle?

The angle is less than 109° because lone pairs, being closer to the central atom, repel more than bonding pairs. With one lone pair, the angle collapses to about 107° and with two lone pairs it collapses further to about 105°.

Turn the page for some exam questions on this topic ➤

For more on this topic, see page 17 of the *Revision Express A-level Study Guide*

Exam question 1

Draw a dot and cross diagram for each molecule. Then draw a stick model for each and work out the angles

For each of the molecules or ions below, draw a diagram to show the shape and indicate all of the bond angles.

CH_4 — 109°

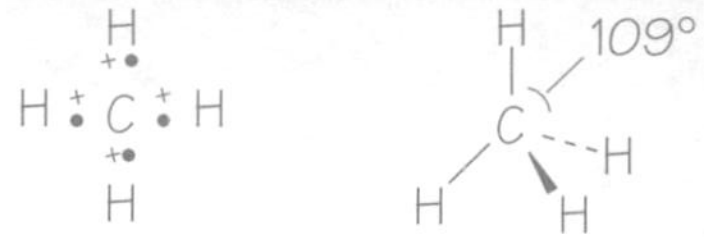

CO_2 — O=C=O, 180°

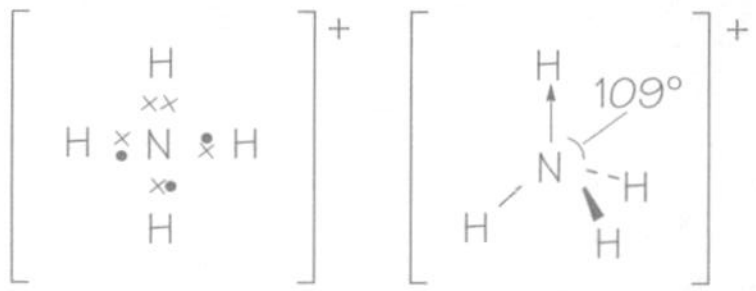

NH_4^+ — 109°

$BeCl_2$ — Cl—Be—Cl, 180°

SF_6 — 90°

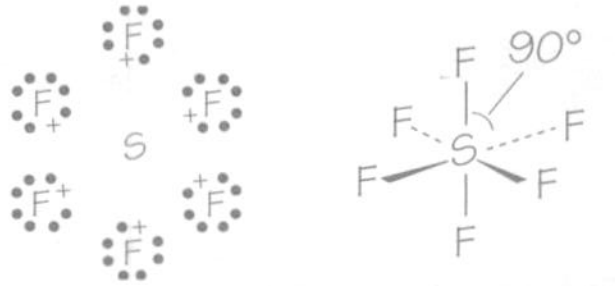

DON'T FORGET
Draw a dot and cross diagram for the molecule. Count the number of electron pairs around the central atom. Count the number of lone pairs.

SYLLABUS CHECK
Edexcel and AQA require a little bit more than the other boards. Make sure that you can also draw the SO_4^{2-}, NO_3^-, CO_3^{2-} ions and the bipyramidal PCl_5 molecule.

Exam question 2

Use diagrams to help you explain why BF_3 is a non-polar molecule whereas NH_3 is said to be polar.

First draw dot and cross diagrams.

Now draw stick diagrams that show the shape.

Label each atom to show the polarity of each bond. Use δ+ or δ− to show this. Remember electronegativity increases across the period.

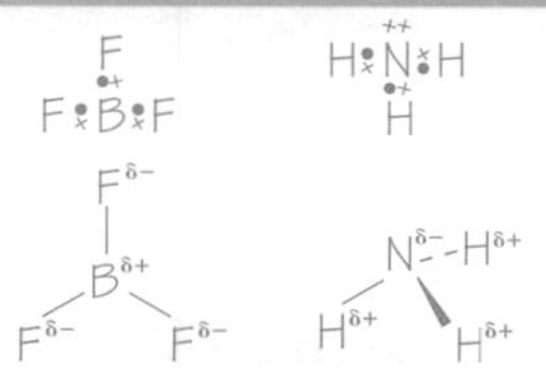

The molecule is non-polar if the individual dipoles cancel out but polar if they do not. The shape helps you decide.

In BF_3 the dipoles cancel out, so the molecule is non-polar but in NH_3 they do not, making this molecule polar.

AS OCR Edexcel AQA WJEC CCEA

Intermolecular forces

These are the forces that hold discrete, covalently bonded molecules together and which determine properties such as melting and boiling temperatures and solubility in water. They are van der Waals forces, permanent dipoles and hydrogen bonding.

Bond polarity and permanent dipoles

The existence of permanent dipoles in a molecule means that molecules are attracted to one another, and this means melting and boiling temperatures are higher than you might otherwise predict.

For each of these molecules, draw the shape of the molecule, mark on any polar bonds and label the molecule as polar or non-polar

Cl_2	Cl — Cl	Non-polar the electrons are shared equally
HCl	$H^{\delta+}$ — $Cl^{\delta-}$	Polar Cl more electronegative than H
CCl_4	$C^{\delta+}$ bonded to four $Cl^{\delta-}$	Non-polar all bonds are polar but they cancel out

THE JARGON
Molecules that are polar are said to have a permanent dipole.

Van der Waals forces

Even if molecules are not polar, they will still have van der Waals forces attracting them together; van der Waals forces are temporary dipoles.

Explain what you understand by the term 'temporary dipole'.

At any moment, the electrons of a particle may not be evenly spaced around it. This causes the particle to have a temporary dipole. A temporary dipole can induce a temporary dipole in a neighbouring particle and so they are attracted.

Hydrogen bonding

This is an especially strong attraction that occurs between a polar hydrogen on one molecule and a lone pair of electrons present on a very electronegative atom of another molecule.

SPEED LEARNING
Hydrogen bonding can only occur when hydrogen is directly attached to **n**itrogen, **o**xygen or **f**luorine. Remember **NOF**.

Draw a diagram to show how hydrogen bonding occurs between two water molecules.

$H^{\delta+}$ — $O^{\delta-}$ — $H^{\delta+}$ ∿∿∿ $H^{\delta+}$ — $O^{\delta-}$ — $H^{\delta+}$

Turn the page for some exam questions on this topic ➤

For more on this topic, see pages 16–21 of the *Revision Express A-level Study Guide*

Exam question 1

Explain the following statements.

(a) The noble gases all have low boiling temperatures but the boiling temperature increases as you go down the group

Boiling temperatures are low because the bonding between atoms of a noble gas will be van der Waals forces, which are very weak. As you go down the group, the number of electrons increases, which increases the strength of the van der Waals forces. This explains the increasing boiling temperature down the group.

DON'T FORGET
To explain the physical properties of a substance you need to work out what types of bonding and structure are present.

(b) Water is a liquid

The bonding in water is covalent, but the simple molecules are held together by hydrogen bonding. Hydrogen bonding is much stronger than van der Waals forces and this gives water a higher than expected melting temperature. The hydrogen bonds are constantly being made and broken as water molecules move past each other.

DON'T FORGET
There's a particularly strong intermolecular force that could account for this. See if you can remember it.

SYLLABUS CHECK
Edexcel also needs you to be able to draw a diagram of ice.

(c) Ice floats on water

Ice is less dense than water. As water is cooled to its melting temperature, the molecules move more slowly and the hydrogen bonding between molecules becomes permanent, forming a very open framework in which the molecules are less closely packed than in the water below.

DON'T FORGET
Ask yourself why one substance floats in another substance. Try to explain what could cause this.

(d) Methane is a gas

Methane is covalently bonded. Covalent bonds are strong, but weak van der Waals forces hold individual molecules together. This is a small molecule with a small number of electrons, so the van der Waals forces are very weak.

DON'T FORGET
Methane is CH_4.

(e) Ethanol (CH_3CH_2OH) will mix well with water, but its isomer methoxymethane (CH_3OCH_3) will not

These two molecules have the same number of electrons, so the van der Waals forces are of the same size. Ethanol is able to hydrogen bond with water but methoxymethane is unable to. (H is connected to O in alcohol, so hydrogen bonding can occur.) In CH_3OCH_3 there are no hydrogen atoms directly attached to N, O or F, so hydrogen bonding cannot occur.

THE JARGON
Isomers have the same molecular formula but different structures.

DON'T FORGET
CH_3OCH_3 is a gas at room temperature.

AS OCR Edexcel AQA WJEC CCEA

Giant structures

Why is diamond so hard if the bonding in carbon is covalent? Why do metals conduct? Why is it that only some substances dissolve in water?

Diamond and graphite ○○○

Label these diagrams to show which is the diamond structure and which is the graphite structure.

In these two forms of carbon, the carbon atoms are held together by covalent bonds in a giant lattice.

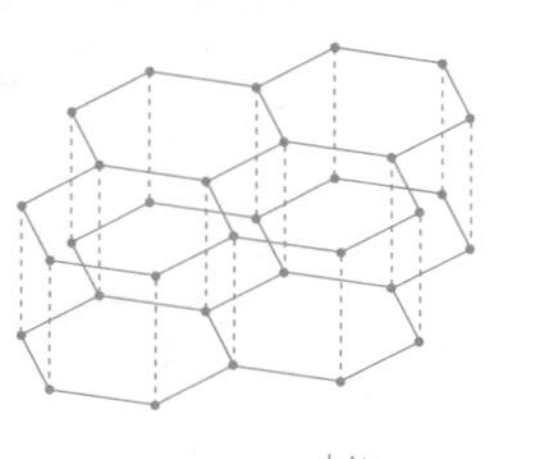
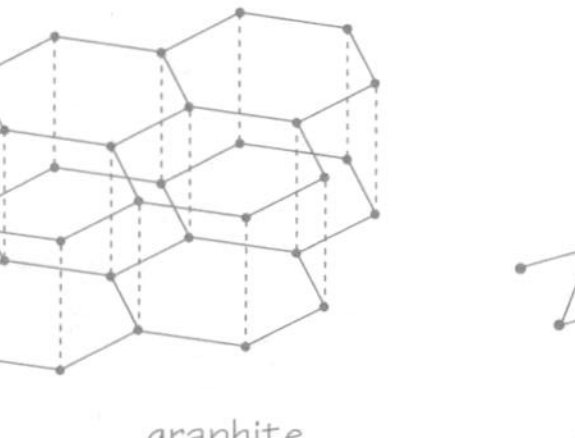
graphite

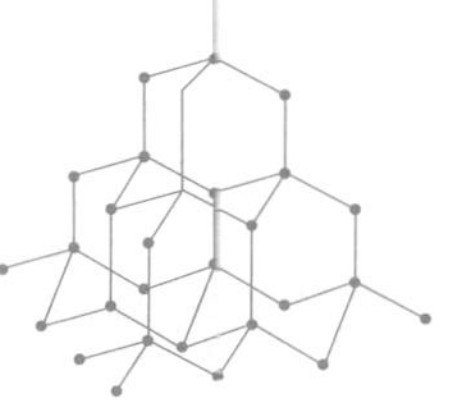
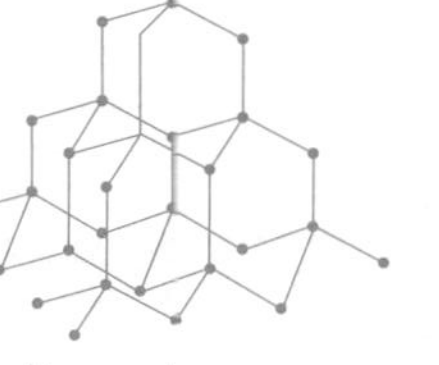
diamond

Tick the statements about diamond and graphite that are correct.

- ☐ Diamond conducts electricity because it is a giant lattice
- ☑ Graphite conducts electricity because one of the electrons on each carbon is delocalized between layers
- ☑ There is strong bonding within a layer of graphite but there are only weak attractions between layers
- ☐ The bonds in diamond are easily broken because they are covalent
- ☑ Diamond cannot conduct because all of the electrons are localized in bonds

SYLLABUS CHECK
For CCEA you need to know that quartz also consists of a giant lattice, with Si and O covalently bonded.

Metallic bonding ○○○

Use these words to construct a statement that describes metallic bonding: mobile, lattice, bonding, electrons, ions, giant, attraction, sea, metallic, electrostatic.

In metallic bonding there is a giant metallic lattice, where there is a strong electrostatic attraction between a lattice of positive ions and a sea of mobile electrons.

Relating structure and bonding to properties ○○○

Place a T beside a statement if it is true and a tick beside the explanation if it is correct.

Statement		Explanation	
Ionic compounds have high melting temperatures	T	A strong attraction between oppositely charged ions	✓
Metals conduct electricity	T	Their ions are free to move	
Simple molecular compounds have low melting temperatures	T	This is because they are covalently bonded	
Ionic compounds conduct electricity when molten	T	Their ions are free to move when molten	✓
Boiling temperature of noble gases increases as you go down the group	T	Increasing strength of van der Waals forces as number of electrons increases	✓

Turn the page for some exam questions on this topic ➤

For more on this topic, see page 15 of the *Revision Express A-level Study Guide*

Exam question 1 ●●●

Describe the bonding and structure in sodium chloride, diamond and iodine. Draw diagrams to show each structure. Describe and explain their physical properties.

First work out what type of bonding will be in each and what type of structure it has. Next draw a diagram of each structure.

	Sodium chloride	Diamond	Iodine
Bonding	ionic	covalent	covalent
Structure	giant	giant	simple molecular
Diagram	• Na^+ ● Cl^-		

SYLLABUS CHECK
OCR and Edexcel do not require knowledge of iodine's structure. Check your own syllabus to see if it specifies other structures you should know.

Then I would start to describe and explain the properties of each. Do this for each in turn. List the key points and reasoning.

Your final answer could be given in a table like this. It certainly helps to keep you focused.

SYLLABUS CHECK
Edexcel does not require details of solubility.

Properties of sodium chloride	Explanation of properties
Melting/boiling temperatures high	Strong electrostatic attraction between oppositely charged ions
Conducts electricity when aqueous or molten	Ions free to move
Dissolves in polar solvents, e.g. water	Attraction between charged ions and polar water molecules

Properties of diamond	Explanation of properties
Melting/boiling temperatures high	Lattice held together by strong covalent bonds
Non-conductor of electricity	Electrons localized in bonds, so cannot move
Does not easily dissolve	Lattice too strong for solvent to pull apart

SYLLABUS CHECK
OCR and Edexcel do not require knowledge of iodine's structure or properties.

Properties of iodine	Explanation of properties
Melting/boiling temperature low	Iodine solid but only held together by weak van der Waals forces
Non-conductor of electricity	Electrons localized in bonds so cannot move
Dissolves in non-polar solvents but not in water	No attraction for water since no charges; small molecules easily mix with non-polar solvent

AS OCR Edexcel AQA WJEC CCEA

Starting energetics

Energy may be taken in during a reaction (endothermic) or energy may be given out during a reaction (exothermic). The study of these energy changes is known as energetics. These changes are called *enthalpy* changes.

Enthalpy profile diagrams

These changes are often shown on enthalpy profile diagrams.

Label one of these diagrams as endothermic and the other as exothermic. Label the activation energy on both.

THE JARGON
The activation energy is the minimum energy that colliding particles must have in order for a reaction to occur.

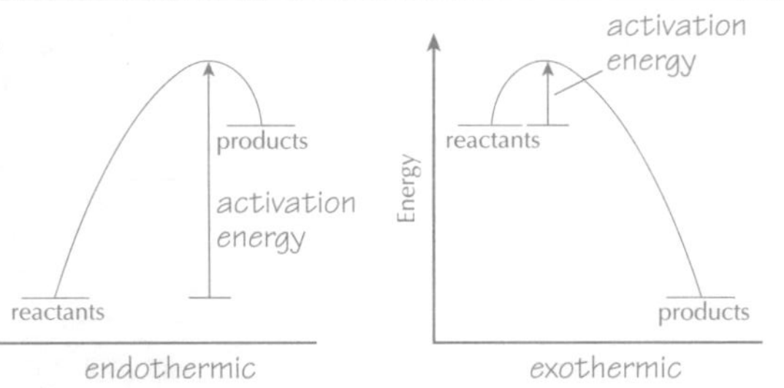

For each reaction given, tick the correct column to say whether the reaction is endothermic or exothermic.

	Endothermic	Exothermic
Methane burning		✓
Respiration		✓
Decomposing calcium carbonate	✓	
Photosynthesis	✓	
Magnesium reacting with acid		✓

Bond breaking and making

Bond breaking is always **endothermic.**
Bond making is always **exothermic.**

Highlight the key points in this statement.

A measure of the amount of energy stored in a chemical system is the enthalpy (*H*) and enthalpy changes (ΔH) that can be measured when reactions occur. In an exothermic reaction, energy is given out; it is lost to the surroundings and ΔH is negative (−ve).

Define what is meant by these terms.

Enthalpy change of formation, ΔH_f

The energy change when 1 mole of a substance forms from its constituent elements, in their standard states, under standard conditions.

Standard conditions

100 kPa (1 atmosphere) pressure and a stated temperature, e.g. 298 K.

Enthalpy of combustion, ΔH_c

The enthalpy change that occurs when 1 mole of a substance burns completely in oxygen under standard conditions.

THE JARGON
Average bond enthalpy is the average energy needed to break one mole of a specified type of covalent bonds.

Turn the page for some exam questions on this topic ➤

For more on this topic, see pages 30–35 of the *Revision Express A-level Study Guide*

Exam question 1

Use the bond enthalpies below to calculate the enthalpy of combustion of methane.

First you must write a balanced equation using displayed formulae.

THE JARGON
A displayed formula shows the placing of bonds and the type of bond between each atom.

WATCH OUT
Bond enthalpies always have positive ΔH values since, by definition, bonds are broken.

Bond	Average bond enthalpy (kJ mol^{-1})
C–C	+347
C–H	+413
C=O	+805
H–O	+464
O=O	+498

$$\text{H–C(H)(H)–H} + 2\,\text{O=O} \rightarrow \text{O=C=O} + 2\,\text{H–O–H}$$

Now write down two headings side by side, one for bonds broken and one for bonds made. Work out how many of each type of bond are broken and made.

Bonds broken (ΔH positive) in kJ mol^{-1}	Bonds made (ΔH negative) in kJ mol^{-1}
4 C—H = 4 × (+413)	2 C=O = 2 × (−805)
2 O=O = 2 × (+498)	4 H—O = 4 × (−464)

Find the total energy taken in as bonds are broken, and the total energy given out as bonds form.

Total energy needed = +2 648 kJ mol^{-1} Total energy given out = −3 466 kJ mol^{-1}

Add these totals together to get the overall enthalpy change.

Overall change = +2 648 + (−3 466 kJ)
= **−818 kJ mol^{-1}**

Think of the values you are using.

A data book gives the enthalpy of combustion as −890 kJ mol^{-1}. Can you explain why the value you have calculated above is different (and less correct)?

DON'T FORGET
It is the high strength of the C=O bond that is largely responsible for the overall change in enthalpy being negative (exothermic).

The value of **−818 kJ mol^{-1}** was calculated using **average** bond energies, so calculations using them will only ever give an approximate answer.

Draw an enthalpy profile for this reaction.

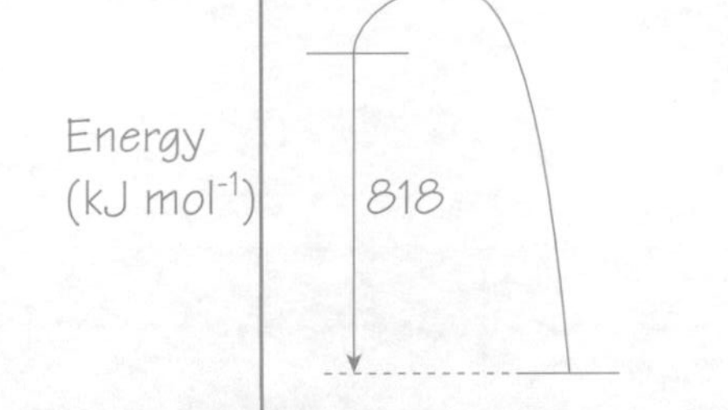

Calculating enthalpy changes

You will have carried out experiments to measure some enthalpy changes and will have used Hess's law in calculations.

Measuring enthalpy of combustion, ΔH_c, by experiment

This will involve burning a fuel, heating some water and measuring its temperature rise.

List the measurements you need to make.

You need to measure mass of fuel before and after, mass of water heated, temperature of water before and after.

You will also need to know the specific heat capacity of the water.

You will need to use the equation: $Q = mc\Delta T$. For each quantity in this equation, say what it is and give its units.

Symbol	Quantity	Units
Q	energy	J
m	mass of water	g
c	specific heat capacity	$J\ g^{-1}\ °C^{-1}$
ΔT	change in temperature	°C

Try this question. Hide the hints if you don't need them.

100.0 g water at 20 °C were heated to 100 °C using a spirit burner containing ethanol. The mass of ethanol used was 1.20 g. Calculate the enthalpy of combustion for ethanol. Use $c = 4.18\ J\ g^{-1}\ °C^{-1}$.

Calculate the energy given to the water.

$Q = mc\Delta T = 100.0 \times 4.18 \times 80$
$= 33.44$ kJ given to water

Find the number of moles of ethanol burnt.

$n = 1.20/46.3 = 0.0259$ mol C_2H_5OH

Find the energy given to the water per mole of ethanol burnt.

Energy per mol of ethanol burnt
$= 33.44/0.0259$
$= 1290\ kJ\ mol^{-1}$

What is ΔH_c for ethanol?

$\Delta H_c = -1290\ kJ\ mol^{-1}$
The chemical system has lost this energy.

Hess's law

This is used to find enthalpy changes that cannot be measured directly.

The jargon

Hess's law states that the overall energy change does not depend on the route taken, but only on the initial and final conditions.

$$\tfrac{1}{2}O_{2(g)} + C_{(s)} + \tfrac{1}{2}O_{2(g)} \xrightarrow{\Delta H_1} CO_{(g)} + \tfrac{1}{2}O_{2(g)}$$

ΔH_2 (to $CO_{2(g)}$), ΔH_3 (from CO to $CO_{2(g)}$)

What are ΔH_1, ΔH_2, ΔH_3 in this Hess cycle?

ΔH_1 is the enthalpy of formation, ΔH_f, of CO
ΔH_2 is the enthalpy of formation, ΔH_f, of CO_2
or the enthalpy of combustion, ΔH_c, of $C_{(s)}$
ΔH_3 is the enthalpy of combustion ΔH_c of CO

Write an equation in terms of ΔH_2 and ΔH_3 that would allow you to calculate ΔH_1.

$\Delta H_1 = \Delta H_2 - \Delta H_3$

Turn the page for some exam questions on this topic ➤

For more on this topic, see pages 30–34 of the *Revision Express A-level Study Guide*

Exam question 1

Use the following values of ΔH to find a value for the enthalpy change of formation of propane (C_3H_8).

Write an equation for the value you are trying to find. Then draw an energy cycle beneath it.

Substance	Enthalpy change ($kJ\ mol^{-1}$)
$C_3H_{8(g)}$	$\Delta H_c = -2\,219$
$CO_{2(g)}$	$\Delta H_f = -393$
$H_2O_{(l)}$	$\Delta H_f = -286$

Add oxygen to both sides and draw arrows to form the products of burning. Check the directions of the arrows match the ΔH values you are given.

$$2O_{2(g)} + 3C_{(s)} + 4H_{2(g)} \xrightarrow{\Delta H_f} C_3H_{8(g)} + 2O_{2(g)}$$

Write the enthalpy changes onto the arrows. Remember to take the number of moles into account.

$3(-393)$, $4(-286)$, $-2\,219$

$$3CO_{2(g)} + 4H_2O_{(l)}$$

Write an equation for finding ΔH_f for propane. Reverse the sign for values where you have to go the wrong way along the arrow.

$\Delta H_f = 3(-393) + 4(-286) - (-2\,219)$
$= -104\ kJ\ mol^{-1}$

Exam question 2

Using the following ΔH_f values, calculate an enthalpy change for the reaction of Br_2 with ethene, shown in the equation below. What does this value tell you about the stability of bromoethane compared to bromine and ethene?

$Br_{2(g)} + C_2H_{4(g)} \rightarrow C_2H_4Br_{2(g)}$

Substance	ΔH_f ($kJ\ mol^{-1}$)
$Br_{2(g)}$	+31
$C_2H_{4(g)}$	+52
$C_2H_4Br_{2(g)}$	−38

Watch out

Br_2 does not have ΔH_f of zero as expected for elements. This is because it is not in its standard state in this equation.

First draw a suitable Hess cycle.

$$Br_{2(g)} + C_2H_{4(g)} \xrightarrow{\Delta H_r} C_2H_4Br_{2(g)}$$

ΔH_1, ΔH_2

$$Br_{2(l)} + 2C_{(s)} + 2H_{2(g)}$$

Now write an expression for ΔH_r and substitute the values.

$\Delta H_r = \Delta H_2 - \Delta H_1$
$= -38 - (+31 + 52)$
$= -121\ kJ\ mol^{-1}$

What does a negative value for an enthalpy of reaction tell you?

A negative value tells you that a reaction is likely to happen, though it does not tell you how fast. The negative value means that bromoethane is stable with respect to bromine and ethene.

Rates of reaction

The study of how fast a reaction proceeds is sometimes called kinetics. You need to know the factors that affect the rate of a reaction and why they do so.

LINKS
For a reminder of how activation energy is defined, see p. 21.

Collision theory

For a successful reaction to occur, particles must collide and they must collide with enough energy to break existing bonds; in other words, they must overcome the activation energy.

Factors that affect the rate of a reaction

Link the change in the first column with the effect in the second by joining the *.

Change			Effect
Increase temperature	* 1	* 2	Molecules collide more often
Increase gas pressure	* 2	* 1	Particles collide more often and with more energy
Increase solution concentration	* 3	* 3	Particles collide more often
Add a catalyst	* 4	* 5	Larger surface over which reaction can occur
Increase surface area of solid reactants	* 5	* 4	Lowers the activation energy

The Maxwell–Boltzmann distribution

This shows the range of energies that molecules of a gas may have at a given temperature, T_1. The area under the curve shows the total number of particles present. On the energy axis, E_a represents the activation energy.

On this graph, shade in the area which shows those molecules that have sufficient energy to react successfully at temperature T_1.

Draw another curve to show the distribution at a higher temperature, T_2, and using a different colour, shade in the proportion of molecules that can now overcome the activation barrier.

Fraction of molecules

T_1

T_2

E_a

Energy

Fraction of molecules with sufficient energy to react at T_1

Fraction of molecules with sufficient energy to react at T_2

Use your graph to explain why small increases in temperature can lead to large increases in rate of reaction.

Heating a gas causes the average kinetic energy of the molecules to increase, and at this higher temperature the Maxwell–Boltzmann distribution is displaced to the right. This means there are now more molecules that have sufficient energy to overcome the activation energy, so there are more successful collisions.

Turn the page for some exam questions on this topic ➤

For more on this topic, see pages 48–49 of the *Revision Express A-level Study Guide*

Exam question 1

An excess of zinc granules and 100 cm^3 of 0.1 mol dm^{-3} hydrochloric acid were reacted. The volume of hydrogen formed was measured at 1 minute intervals and here are the results.

Time (min)	Volume H_2 (cm^3)	Time (min)	Volume H_2 (cm^3)
0	0	6	102
1	20	7	111
2	42	8	118
3	62	9	120
4	79	10	120
5	90		

You should always plot the independent variable (the one you control) on the *x*-axis and the dependent variable (the one you are measuring) on the *y*-axis.

(a) Plot a graph of these results.
(b) Sketch onto your graph the following labelled curves for experiments carried out at the same temperature.
P 100 cm^3 of 0.1 mol dm^{-3} HCl, excess powdered Zn
Q 50 cm^3 of 0.1 mol dm^{-3} HCl, excess powdered Zn
R 100 cm^3 of 0.1 mol dm^{-3} HCl, excess powdered Zn with a $CuSO_4$ catalyst

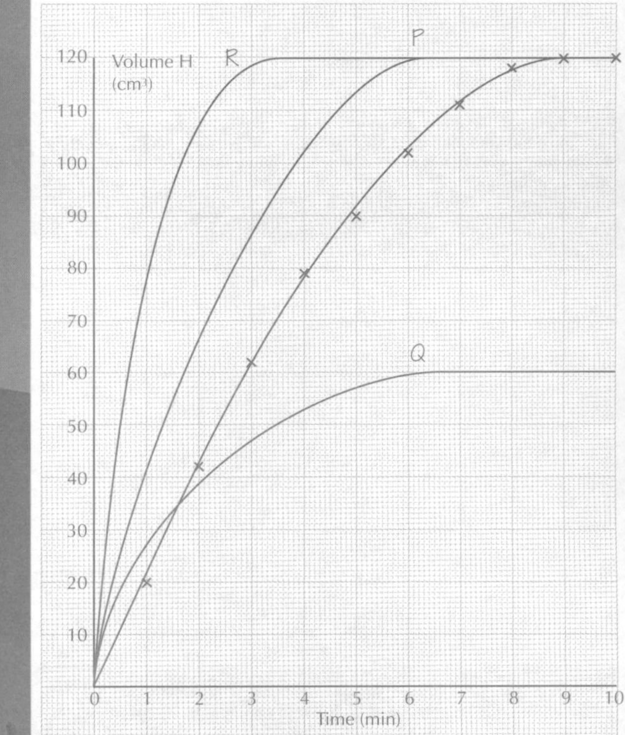

Using catalysts

AS OCR (Edexcel AQA) WJEC CCEA

Catalysts are substances that alter the rate of a reaction without being used up themselves. They have considerable economic importance.

How does a catalyst work?

Catalysts provide an easier route for the reaction, with a lower activation energy. Add this information to the diagram of the Maxwell–Boltzmann distribution then use collision theory to explain why the rate of reaction increases.

As the diagram shows, lowering the activation energy means that a higher proportion of molecules now have enough energy to undergo successful collisions, so the reaction rate increases.

The effect of using a catalyst can also be shown on an enthalpy profile for a reaction.

On this enthalpy profile, sketch in the effect of using a catalyst.

THE JARGON
In homogeneous catalysis the catalyst is in the same phase as the reactants, whereas in heterogeneous catalysis the catalyst and reactants are in different phases.

LINKS
For more detail on the effects of CFCs on ozone, see pp. 71–72.

Homogeneous catalysis

Give an example of homogeneous catalysis.

Chlorine free radicals reacting to deplete ozone and H^+ ions in esterification.

SYLLABUS CHECK
OCR, WJEC and CCEA only.

Heterogeneous catalysis

Iron is used in the Haber process for converting nitrogen and hydrogen to ammonia.

N2(g) 1 3H2(g) ⇌ 2NH3(g)

Number the stages in this argument, which explains how the catalyst works.

The molecules react to form NH_3	5
This causes the reaction to have a high activation energy	2
The triple bond in nitrogen is very strong	1
The bonding is not so strong that it does not release the NH_3 gas formed	6
The bonding is strong enough to weaken bonds in H_2 and N_2	4
H_2 and N_2 are adsorbed onto the iron surface	3

THE JARGON
Adsorbed means the substance is taken up by the surface of the catalyst.

Turn the page for some exam questions on this topic ➤

For more on this topic, see pages 50–51 of the *Revision Express A-level Study Guide*

Exam question 1

Define the following terms.

Catalyst

This is a substance that changes the speed of a chemical reaction without itself being used up.

Homogeneous catalyst

A catalyst that is in the same phase as the reactants.

Heterogeneous catalyst

A catalyst that is in a different phase from the reactants.

Activation energy

This is the minimum energy that colliding particles must possess to have a successful collision.

SYLLABUS CHECK
AQA and Edexcel do not require you to know the terms homogeneous and heterogeneous at AS.

Exam question 2

An important application of catalysis is the removal of pollutants from car exhausts by catalytic converters. Write an account of this process. You should include details of the pollutants, the nature of the catalyst and its mode of action.

SYLLABUS CHECK
OCR needs this in detail and CCEA in outline.

What are the pollutants?

The pollutants are carbon monoxide, unburnt hydrocarbons and nitrogen oxides; they can produce photochemical smog and low-level ozone, which may cause respiratory problems.

How do they come to be in exhaust gases?

The high temperatures of the internal combustion engine cause N_2 from the air to combine with O_2 from the air. CO and hydrocarbons result from incomplete combustion.

What is the nature of the catalyst?

A heterogeneous catalyst of Rh/Pt/Pd is used.

How does the catalyst work? To give you a hint, it's a three-step process.

The catalyst **adsorbs** carbon monoxide and nitrogen oxide on the surface. This causes **weakening** of bonds and allows the reaction between CO and NO at the surface. **Desorption** of nitrogen and carbon dioxide then occurs at the surface, releasing the products.

Write an equation for the reaction between CO and NO.

$2CO_{(g)} + 2NO_{(g)} \rightarrow 2CO_{2(g)} + N_{2(g)}$

AS OCR Edexcel AQA WJEC CCEA

Equilibrium

Many reactions are reversible – they can go forwards and backwards. When a balance is reached between the rate of the forward reaction and the rate of the reverse reaction, we say that the system is in equilibrium.

SYLLABUS CHECK
CCEA students should make sure they can carry out calculations involving K_c and K_p. Other students will meet them next year.

Dynamic equilibrium

In the contact process for the formation of sulphuric acid, one of the stages is the formation of SO_3 from SO_2; this is an equilibrium reaction.

Write an equation for this process. Include state symbols.

$2SO_{2(g)} + O_{2(g)} \qquad 2SO_{3(g)}$

Put a tick against the boxes that contain true statements about this equilibrium.

Statement	
During the reaction, molecules of SO_2 and O_2 react to make SO_3 at the same time as SO_3 molecules decompose to make SO_2 and O_2 molecules	✓
At equilibrium the forward and reverse reactions stop	☐
At equilibrium the forward and reverse reactions are occurring at equal rates	✓
At equilibrium there is no apparent change in the proportions of each gas present	✓
Once equilibrium is reached, we cannot affect the position of equilibrium	☐
A catalyst will alter the position of equilibrium and affect the yield of product	☐
Catalysts do not affect the position of equilibrium; they just make the forward and reverse reactions occur faster	✓
Equilibrium will be reached faster if a catalyst is used	✓
A catalyst of vanadium(V) oxide is used in the contact process	✓
Any statement can only be true if we are talking about a closed system	✓

THE JARGON
A closed system is one where no reactants or products can leave or enter the system.

Le Chatelier's principle

Le Chatelier stated that if a closed system in equilibrium is exposed to a change in conditions, then the position of equilibrium will alter in order to minimize the effect of that change.

The reaction $2SO_{2(g)} + O_{2(g)} \rightleftharpoons 2SO_{3(g)}$ is exothermic.

State whether the following changes would increase or decrease the yield of SO_3 and say why.

Change	Effect
Increase the temperature (T)	Decreases yield to restore T, the reverse reaction, which is endothermic, occurs
Increase the pressure (P)	Increases yield 3 mol gas form 2 mol gas, and this reduces P
Use V_2O_5, a catalyst	No effect on yield

Turn the page for some exam questions on this topic ➤

For more on this topic, see pages 56–60 of the *Revision Express A-level Study Guide*

Exam question 1

Use the steps below to develop your answer.

In the Haber process, nitrogen and hydrogen are reacted to form ammonia. Describe this process, paying particular attention to the conditions used in order to achieve a good yield of ammonia at a reasonable rate.

Write a balanced equation for this process, including state symbols.

$N_{2(g)} + 3H_{2(g)} \rightleftharpoons 2NH_{3(g)}$

Conditions for a fast rate

Say what conditions are needed to get a fast rate of reaction.

High pressure
High temperature
Use a catalyst

Conditions for a high yield

State and explain the conditions needed for a high yield. The reaction is exothermic.

High pressure: 4 mol of gas go to 2 mol gas, so if the reaction goes forward, the pressure drops
Low temperature: if you lower the temperature, the equilibrium will shift to restore it by going forwards

Actual conditions

Give the actual conditions used in this process.

Pressure	200 atm
Temperature	450 °C
Catalyst	iron

These conditions are used for the following reasons:

Why are these conditions used?

For a high yield, a low temperature is needed, but this leads to a slow rate. A compromise of 450 °C is used along with a catalyst.

For a high yield, a high pressure is needed. This is also good for the rate. The higher the pressure, the more expensive the chemical plant needed to maintain it, so the pressure is made relatively high but not extremely high – another compromise.

What is all the ammonia needed for?

Tick the boxes to show which of the following items are made from the ammonia obtained in the Haber process.

Item	
Explosives	✓
Natural gas	☐
Fertilizers	✓
Extracting aluminium	☐
Polyamides like nylon	✓
Sulphuric acid	☐

Acids and bases

AS OCR CCEA

A useful definition of an acid is a proton (H^+) donor, and a useful definition of a base is a proton acceptor. This is known as the Brønsted–Lowry theory.

SYLLABUS CHECK
The reactions of acids and bases are assumed knowledge from GCSE for most syllabuses, so it is a good idea to review them here. OCR lists these reactions on its syllabus.

Strong and weak acids and bases

A strong acid fully dissociates into its ions but a weak acid only partially dissociates. A strong base fully dissociates into its ions but a weak base only partially dissociates.

For each equation, state whether the substance in bold is an acid or base and whether it is strong or weak.

$\mathbf{HCl_{(aq)}} \rightarrow H^+_{(aq)} + Cl^-_{(aq)}$	strong acid
$\mathbf{NH_{3(aq)}} + H_2O_{(l)} \rightleftharpoons NH^+_{4(aq)} + OH^-_{(aq)}$	weak base
$\mathbf{NaOH_{(aq)}} \rightarrow Na^+_{(aq)} + OH^-_{(aq)}$	strong base
$\mathbf{CH_3CO_2H_{(aq)}} \rightleftharpoons CH_3CO^-_{2(aq)} + H^+_{(aq)}$	weak acid

Typical reactions of acids and bases

Complete these general word equations.

ACID + METAL → salt + hydrogen
ACID + BASE → salt + water
ACID + ALKALI → salt + water
ACID + CARBONATE → salt + water + carbon dioxide

THE JARGON
An alkali is a soluble base; salts form when a metal displaces the hydrogen of an acid.

Write word equations for the following reactions. Do not learn specific equations; learn the general equations and apply them to specific cases.

magnesium + sulphuric acid → magnesium sulphate + hydrogen
copper (II) oxide + hydrochloric acid → copper (II) chloride + water
ammonia solution + sulphuric acid → ammonium sulphate
sodium carbonate + nitric acid → sodium nitrate + carbon dioxide + water

General equation for neutralization of an acid by a base.

Whenever an acid reacts with a base, an ionic equation can be written that shows the hydrogen ion reacting with the hydroxide ion. Write this ionic equation.

$$H^+_{(aq)} + OH^-_{(aq)} \rightarrow H_2O_{(l)}$$

When 50 cm^3 of 2.0 mol dm^{-3} HCl react with 50 cm^3 of 2.0 mol dm^{-3} NaOH, the temperature rises by 13.0 °C. Calculate $\Delta H_{neutralization}$

Energy given to solution	$= 100 \times 4.18 \times 13.0 = 5\,434$ J
Energy lost by chemical system	$= -5\,434$ J
Amount of acid	$= 2.0 \times 50/1\,000 = 0.10$ mol
Energy per mole of H^+ neutralized	$= -5\,434/0.1 =$ **−54.3 kJ mol^{-1}**

LINKS
For a reminder of how to calculate enthalpy changes, see p. 23.

WATCH OUT
When calculating enthalpies of neutralization, think carefully about the mass of solution that is heated.

Turn the page for some exam questions on this topic ➤

For more on this topic, see page 66 of the *Revision Express A-level Study Guide*

Exam question 1

One use for ammonia is to produce fertilizers. The ammonia is used as a source of the nitrogen needed for plant growth but ammonia itself is not applied directly to the soil; instead salts such as ammonium nitrate or ammonium sulphate are applied.

Write a balanced symbol equation for the reaction of ammonia with nitric acid to form ammonium nitrate, NH_4NO_3. Include state symbols.

$$NH_{3(aq)} + HNO_{3(aq)} \rightarrow NH_4NO_{3(aq)}$$

How is ammonia acting as a Bronsted-Lowry base?

SYLLABUS CHECK
AQA and Edexcel do not require you to know about Brønsted–Lowry theory.

It is acting as a proton acceptor.

$$NH_3 + H^+_{(aq)} \rightarrow NH^+_{4(aq)}$$

Write a balanced symbol equation for the reaction of ammonia to form ammonium sulphate, $(NH_4)_2SO_4$. Include state symbols.

$$2NH_{3(aq)} + H_2SO_{4(aq)} \rightarrow (NH_4)_2SO_{4(aq)}$$

Suggest two reasons why ammonia is not applied directly to fields.

It is volatile, so it would not remain in the soil.
It is an alkali, so it would kill soil organisms and give a pH too high for good crop growth.

How do the percentages (%) of nitrogen in ammonium nitrate and ammonium sulphate compare? Show your working. Use these values of A_r: N = 14.0, O = 16.0, H = 1.0, S = 32.1.

Find the molar mass of each and then calculate the percentage of this mass that is composed of nitrogen.

M_r NH_4NO_3 = 14.0 + 4.0 + 14.0 + 48.0 = 80.0
% N = 28.0/80.0 × 100% = 35%

M_r $(NH_4)_2SO_4$ = 28.0 + 8.0 + 32.1 + 64.0 = 132.1
% N = 28.0/132.1 × 100% = 21%

There is 14% more nitrogen by mass in ammonium nitrate than in ammonium sulphate.

LINKS
To remind yourself of how to calculate molar mass, see p. 7.

DON'T FORGET
After you've calculated the percentages of nitrogen, make a comparison.

AS OCR Edexcel AQA WJEC CCEA

Redox reactions

Redox reactions occur when reduction and oxidation take place together. A substance that causes oxidation is an oxidizing agent and one that causes reduction is a reducing agent.

SYLLABUS CHECK
If you study CCEA, you also need to be able to use standard electrode potential values.

Assigning oxidation numbers

By assigning oxidation numbers (states) to elements, we can see whether oxidation or reduction has occurred.

Say whether these statements are true or false. If they are false, explain why. Check your answers before you move on to the next section.

In compounds, fluorine always has an oxidation number of +1	False, it's −1
The oxidation number of an ion of an element is equal to its charge	True
In compounds, oxygen usually has an oxidation number of −2 and hydrogen +1	True
In complex ions the total of all the oxidation numbers is equal to the charge	True
When assigning oxidation numbers in a compound or complex ion, always assign the least electronegative atoms first	False, begin with the most electronegative
The oxidation number of all elements is 0	True
In metal hydrides, such as lithium hydride, hydrogen has an oxidation number of +1	False, it's −1

LINKS
For a definition of electronegativity, see p. 11.

In each of these formulae, work out the oxidation state of the element in bold type.

$\mathbf{P}_2O_5$	O = (5 × −2) so each P = +5
$K\mathbf{Mn}O_4$	K = +1, O = (4 × −2) so Mn = +7
$\mathbf{Cr}Cl_3$	Cl = (3 × −1) so Cr = +3
$K_2\mathbf{Cr}_2O_7$	K = (2 × +1), O = (7 × −2) so each Cr = +6
$\mathbf{Cr}O_4^{2-}$	−2 overall, O = (4 × −2) so Cr = +6
$Na\mathbf{H}$	Na = +1 so H = −1

THE JARGON
When hydrogen is combined with a metal, the compound is called a hydride.

Oxidation and reduction

Say whether these statements are true or false and if false, explain why.

Oxidation number increases when oxidation occurs	True
Oxidation number decreases when reduction occurs	True
Electrons are lost during oxidation and electrons are gained during reduction	True

SPEED LEARNING
OILRIG: oxidation is loss of electrons, reduction is gain of electrons.

When Cr reacts with Cl_2 we can see that redox is occurring because the oxidation number of Cr goes *up* from 0 to +3; the oxidation number of Cl_2 goes *down* from 0 to −1.

Write a balanced equation for this reaction; label the oxidation states on Cr and Cl. Indicate the reduction and oxidation with labelled arrows.

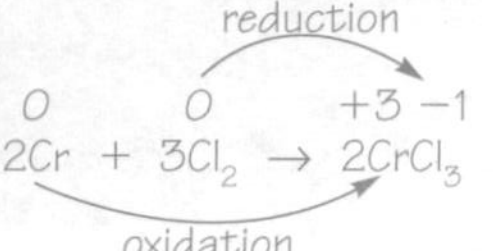

Turn the page for some exam questions on this topic ➤

For more on this topic, see pages 76–77 of the *Revision Express A-level Study Guide*

Exam question 1

The reaction of NO and CO brought about by the catalytic converter in a car exhaust is a redox reaction. The products are nitrogen and carbon dioxide. Write a balanced equation for this reaction and identify the substance that is oxidized.

You can do this most easily by looking at which substance gains oxygen.

$$2CO_{(g)} + 2NO_{(g)} \rightarrow 2CO_{2(g)} + N_{2(g)}$$

The carbon monoxide is being oxidized since it is gaining oxygen. We can also see that its oxidation number rises from +2 to +4.

Exam question 2

SYLLABUS CHECK
Only AQA needs you to know that titration is a method of determining the amount of iodine present, but all boards except OCR require you to add half-equations like this.

During the titration of I_2 with sodium thiosulphate, $Na_2S_2O_3$, the endpoint is detected when the iodine has all been reduced to I^- ions. The thiosulphate is oxidized to the tetrathionate ion, $S_4O_6^{2-}$.

Write an ion/electron equation for the reduction of iodine.

This is a half-equation.

$$I_2 + 2e^- \rightarrow 2I^-$$

The ion/electron equation for the oxidation is

$$2S_2O_3^{2-} \rightarrow S_4O_6^{2-} + 2e^-.$$

Show that the sulphur has been oxidized.

Look at oxidation numbers.

In $S_2O_3^{2-}$ the overall charge on the ion is −2. The contribution from oxygen is −6, so +4 charge must be spread over two sulphurs. S has an oxidation number of +2 in $S_2O_3^{2-}$. In $S_4O_6^{2-}$ the oxidation number is $+2\frac{1}{2}$, so the oxidation number has increased, showing that oxidation has occurred.

Combine the two equations to write a fully balanced ionic equation for the reaction.

First make sure there is an equal number of electrons in both equations, multiplying any equation as necessary.

$$2S_2O_3^{2-} + I_2 + 2e^- \rightarrow 2I^- + S_4O_6^{2-} + 2e^-$$

Then combine the equations so the electrons cancel out.

$$2S_2O_3^{2-} + I_2 \rightarrow 2I^- + S_4O_6^{2-}$$

WATCH OUT
If you have correctly combined the equations, make sure the atoms balance and the charges balance.

Exam question 3

These equations show three displacement reactions of the halogens:

$$Cl_{2\,(aq)} + 2KBr_{(aq)} \rightarrow 2KCl_{(aq)} + Br_{2\,(aq)}$$
$$Br_{2\,(aq)} + 2KI_{(aq)} \rightarrow 2KBr_{(aq)} + I_{2\,(aq)}$$
$$Cl_{2\,(aq)} + 2KI_{(aq)} \rightarrow 2KCl_{(aq)} + I_{2\,(aq)}$$

What do they show about the oxidizing ability of the halogens?

Look at what happens to the oxidation numbers.

Cl_2 can oxidize Br^- to Br_2 and I^- to I_2, so it is the most oxidizing of the three. Br_2 can oxidize I^- to I_2, so it is more oxidizing than iodine. The order of oxidizing ability is $Cl_2 > Br_2 > I_2$.

AS OCR Edexcel AQA WJEC CCEA

The periodic table

The periodic table is a wonderful tool for chemists, and it's a shame to put it so far into this book. But now you've reached it!

How the periodic table is organized

The periodic table shows all the elements in order of atomic number with an overlying arrangement of elements into vertical groups and horizontal periods.

Add labels for groups 1 to 0; periods 1, 2, 3 and the transition metals. Shade the s block, p block and d block in different colours and add a key below the table.

	1	2		3	4	5	6	7	0
1			H						He
2	Li	Be		B	C	N	O	F	Ne
3	Na	Mg		Al	Si	P	S	Cl	Ar
	K	Ca	Transition metals	Ga	Ge	As	Se	Br	Kr
	Rb	Sr		In	Sn	Sb	Te	I	Xe

Key: s block, p block, d block

Trends across a period

There are repeating trends in physical and chemical properties across a period.

Give each of these graphs a title to show what trend it shows. Choose from these four options: electrical conductivity across period 3, melting point across period 3, atomic radius down group 2, atomic radius across period 3.

Atomic radius down group 2

Melting point across period 3

Electrical conductivity across period 3

Atomic radius across period 3

Turn the page for some exam questions on this topic ➤

For more on this topic, see pages 88–89 of the *Revision Express A-level Study Guide*

Exam question 1

Here is some data about the elements of period 3.

T_B is the boiling point in kelvin and r_A is the atomic radius in nanometres.

	Na	Mg	Al	Si	P	S	Cl	Ar
T_B (K)	371	922	933	1683	317	386	172	84
r_A (nm)	0.191	0.160	0.130	0.118	0.110	0.102	0.099	0.095

Describe and explain the trend in atomic radius across the period.

WATCH OUT
The question asks you to describe *and* explain. Don't forget to do both.

THE JARGON
Screening, sometimes known as shielding, is due to the repulsive effect of electrons. Inner shell electrons will have a repulsive effect on electrons entering an outer shell. The outer electrons are screened from the full attractive force of the nucleus.

The atomic radius	decreases
because the nuclear charge	increases
so the attraction between electrons and nucleus	increases
but the amount of screening	is the same, as electrons enter the same shell

Describe and explain the change in melting point across the period.

When you are asked about melting point, you should link it to structure and bonding. Fill in this table to show the information you would use in your answer.

	Bonding and structure	Effect on melting point
Na to Al	metallic	High, increases from Na to Al with increased number of delocalized valence electrons and decreasing size of ions
Si	giant covalent	Very high, structure held together by strong covalent bonds
P to Cl	covalent, molecular	Low, only weak van der Waals forces between molecules
Ar	atomic	Low, only weak van der Waals forces between atoms; lower than P to Cl since fewer electrons

WATCH OUT
The strength of van der Waals forces depends on the number of electrons. S_8 has the most, then P_4, Cl_2 and lastly Ar. This explains the shape of the graph you labelled on p. 35.

Exam question 2

For each description, state the type of structure and bonding present.

You should be able to interpret data given in terms of the structure and bonding present. Use *all* of the data.

Melts at 698 °C; conducts when molten but not when solid	giant ionic
Melts at 101 °C; does not dissolve in water or conduct	covalent molecular (but large molecule)
Melts at 1 610 °C; hard, does not dissolve, does not conduct.	giant covalent
Melts at 1 660 °C; conducts when solid	metallic

AS OCR Edexcel AQA WJEC CCEA

Interpreting ionization energies

By looking at the way in which ionization energies change, we can use the information to justify the existence of subshells and work out what group an element is in.

Trend across a period

DON'T FORGET
Your definition should contain the words 'gaseous' and 'one mole'.

The first ionization energy of an element is the energy required to remove one mole of electrons from one mole of the gaseous atoms.

$$M_{(g)} \rightarrow M^+_{(g)} + e^-$$

On this sketch graph of first ionization energies, add the outer shell electron configuration.

LINKS
To remind yourself about the basics of ionization energies, see p. 9.

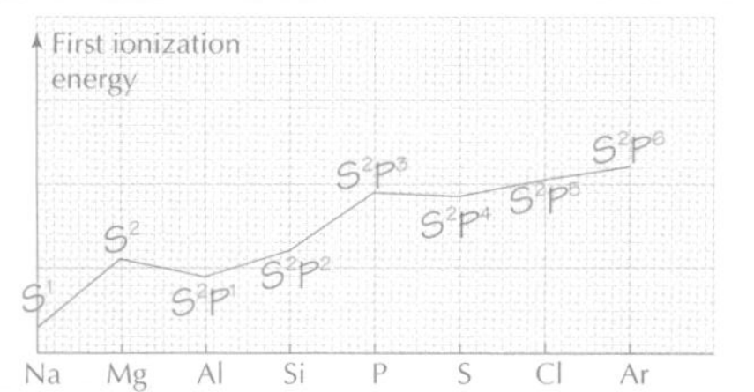

Explain how each of these three factors affects first ionization energy.

Nuclear charge

Increasing the number of protons will increase the attraction, increasing ionization energy.

Distance from nucleus

The further the electron is from the nucleus, the less the attraction, decreasing ionization energy.

Screening

DON'T FORGET
It is the outer electron that's removed.

Outer shell electrons are screened from the nuclear attraction by inner electrons. If screening is present, this makes it easier to remove electrons, reducing ionization energy.

Say whether each of these statements is true or false. If it is false, explain why.

Going down a group, the ionization energy decreases due to increased distance from the nucleus and extra shielding. TRUE

The electrons in boxes notation for the outer electrons of Al, P and S is correctly shown below.

Al $[Ne]3s^23p^1$		P $[Ne]3s^23p^3$		S $[Ne]3s^23p^4$	
3s	3p	3s	3p	3s	3p
⇅	↑ _ _	⇅	↑ ↑ ↑	⇅	⇅ ↑ ↑

TRUE

The first ionization energy of Al is lower than Mg because the 3p orbital is at a higher energy level than the 3s. TRUE

The first ionization energy of S is lower than P because the repulsion caused by spin pairing in the 3p orbital makes it easier to remove this electron. TRUE

Turn the page for some exam questions on this topic ➤

For more on this topic, see page 88 of the *Revision Express A-level Study Guide*

Exam question 1

THE JARGON
Successive ionization energies are for removal of second and subsequent electrons from the gaseous ion.

DON'T FORGET
Ionization energies are always endothermic.

This data shows successive ionization energies for a number of different elements. Study the data then answer the questions.

	Successive ionization energy (kJ mol⁻¹)					
	First	Second	Third	Fourth	Fifth	Sixth
P	419	3 051	4 412	5 877	7 975	9 649
Q	1 012	1 903	2 912	4 957	6 274	21 269
R	496	4 563	6 913	9 544	13 352	16 611
S	578	1 817	2 745	11 578	14 831	18 378

Write an equation to show the first ionization energy for P.

The first ionization energy for P is

$P_{(g)} \rightarrow P^+_{(g)} + e^-$

Write an equation to show the second ionization energy for Q.

The second ionization energy for Q is

$Q^+_{(g)} \rightarrow Q^{2+}_{(g)} + e^-$

Write an equation to show the third ionization energy for R.

The third ionization energy for R is

$R^{2+}_{(g)} \rightarrow R^{3+}_{(g)} + e^-$

How much energy is needed to form a mole of $S^{2+}_{(g)}$ from $S_{(g)}$?

To form S^{2+}, the energy you need is the sum of the first and second ionization energies for S:

$578\ kJ\ mol^{-1} + 1\,817\ kJ\ mol^{-1} = 2\,395\ kJ\ mol^{-1}$

Will this value have a positive or negative sign?

Since energy is required to remove electrons (ionization is always an endothermic process), the sign will be positive.

Which element is in group 5? Explain your reasoning.

Q is in group 5 because there is a big jump up between the fifth and sixth ionization energies. This is when an electron has to be taken from an inner shell. Group 5 elements have five outer electrons to remove before electrons must be taken from an inner shell.

Which two elements are in the same group of the periodic table?

P and R are both in group 1. This is because the large jump in energy required to remove an electron comes after the first ionization energy.

Group 1 – the alkali metals

The elements lithium to caesium in group 1 of the periodic table are soft reactive metals with low melting points. Their characteristic flame colours can be used in analysis.

SYLLABUS CHECK
Although the specific information here is only needed by Edexcel (and a little for CCEA), the general principles discussed apply to group 2 as well.

SYLLABUS CHECK
This is the only aspect of group 1 covered by CCEA.

Flame colours

When compounds containing these elements are heated, the electrons of the metals become excited and are raised into higher energy levels. When the electrons drop back down to their original energy level, they emit the energy as light of specific wavelengths.

Match the flame colour to the metal.

1 lithium	yellow-orange	2
2 sodium	lilac	3
3 potassium	brilliant red	1

Reactions of the elements with oxygen

The elements of group 1 all react with oxygen by losing their outer electron and making oxides. Reactivity increases down the group.

Complete these equations to show the formation of the oxides.

$4Li_{(s)} + O_{2(g)} \rightarrow 2Li_2O_{(s)}$ oxide

$2Na_{(s)} + O_{2(g)} \rightarrow Na_2O_{2(s)}$ peroxide

$K_{(s)} + O_{2(g)} \rightarrow KO_{2(s)}$ superoxide

THE JARGON
Sodium forms the peroxide (O_2^{2-} ion). Potassium forms the superoxide (O_2^- ion).

Reactions of the elements with water

The elements all behave in a similar way to each other, forming hydrogen and alkaline solutions. Reactivity increases down the group.

Write an equation for the reaction of a typical alkali metal, M, with water.

$$2M_{(s)} + 2H_2O_{(l)} \rightarrow 2MOH_{(aq)} + H_{2(g)}$$

LINKS
For a reminder of the reaction between acids and bases, see p. 31.

Reaction of the oxides with water and dilute acid

The oxides react with water to form hydroxides and with acids to form the relevant salt and water.

Write an equation to show the reaction of lithium oxide with water.

$$Li_2O_{(s)} + H_2O_{(l)} \rightarrow 2Li^+_{(aq)} + 2OH^-_{(aq)}$$

Write an equation to show the reaction of Na_2O with dilute sulphuric acid.

$$Na_2O_{(s)} + H_2SO_{4(aq)} \rightarrow Na_2SO_{4(aq)} + H_2O_{(l)}$$

THE JARGON
The polarizing ability is the ability of the cation to distort anions.

Thermal stability of the nitrates and carbonates

The thermal stability of the nitrates and carbonates increases as you go down group 1; this is because the polarizing ability of the cation decreases down the group. Group 1 carbonates, except lithium carbonate, are stable to heat but the nitrates decompose.

For each of these statements, say whether the ability of the cation to polarize the anion will increase or decrease.

Factor increased	Effect on how well cation can polarize
Size of the cation	decrease
Charge on the cation	increase
Size of the anion	increase

Turn the page for some exam questions on this topic ➤

For more on this topic, see pages 90–91 of the *Revision Express A-level Study Guide*

Exam question 1

A group 1 metal (A) is heated in air and rapidly oxidizes, burning with a yellow/orange flame and forming a white solid (B). Water is dripped onto the white solid and an exothermic reaction occurs. Continued addition of water causes a new substance (C) to dissolve. The resulting solution is titrated with nitric acid using an indicator to show when neutralization is complete. The neutral solution contains a salt (D). When a solution of this salt is heated in an evaporating dish to obtain the solid, it decomposes and releases a colourless gas that relights a glowing splint leaving a white solid (E).

Identify substances A to E.

(A) sodium (B) sodium oxide (C) sodium hydroxide
(D) sodium nitrate (E) sodium nitrite

Write four symbol equations for the formation of products B to E.

DON'T FORGET
Sodium nitrite also forms.

$4Na_{(s)} + O_{2(g)} \rightarrow Na_2O_{(s)}$

$Na_2O_{(s)} + H_2O_{(l)} \rightarrow 2NaOH_{(aq)}$

$NaOH_{(aq)} + HNO_{3(aq)} \rightarrow NaNO_{3(aq)} + H_2O_{(l)}$

$2NaNO_{3(s)} \rightarrow 2NaNO_{2(s)} + O_{2(g)}$

Exam question 2

(a) Describe and explain the trend in the ease of decomposition of the nitrates of group 1.
(b) Write symbolic equations to show the decomposition of potassium nitrate and lithium nitrate.

First describe . . .

As you go down group 1, it becomes more difficult to decompose the nitrates.

then explain . . . think in terms of the size and charge of the metal ion as you go down the group.

The metal ion causes distortion of the large nitrate anion; this weakens the N–O bond in nitrates. The ease with which the metal ion can do this is called its polarizing power and it depends on the charge and size of the metal ion. A small highly charged ion has a greater polarizing ability. As you go down group 1, the size of the ion increases; this means there is a decrease in the polarizing effect of the metal ion on the large cation, hence it becomes more difficult to decompose the nitrate.

Now write the equations. Lithium, being at the top of group 1, is very polarizing and causes a greater amount of disruption to the nitrate ion than potassium.

$2KNO_{3(s)} \rightarrow 2KNO_{2(s)} + O_{2(g)}$

$4LiNO_{3(s)} \rightarrow 2Li_2O_{(s)} + 4NO_{2(g)} + O_{2(g)}$

AS OCR Edexcel AQA WJEC CCEA

Group 2

The elements of group 2 are fairly reactive metals; they form compounds in which the oxidation state is +2. Like group 1, they can be identified in compounds from their flame colours.

SYLLABUS CHECK
Flame tests are not needed by OCR.

Flame colours

Match the colour to the metal.

1 calcium	apple green	3
2 strontium	crimson	2
3 barium	brick red	1

SYLLABUS CHECK
If you follow the AQA syllabus, you should check your knowledge of the atypical behaviour of $BeCl_2$ and $Be(OH)_2$.

Reaction of the metal with oxygen and water

All produce ionic oxides when they are burned. Ca, Sr and Ba react with water with increasing vigour, forming hydrogen and alkaline solutions. Mg reacts with steam to form the oxide and hydrogen.

Write general equations for the reactions of a group 2 metal, M, with oxygen and water.

$$2M_{(s)} + O_{2(g)} \rightarrow 2MO_{(s)}$$

$$M_{(s)} + 2H_2O_{(l)} \rightarrow M(OH)_{2(aq)} + H_{2(g)}$$

LINKS
For a reminder of the reaction between metals and acids, see p. 31.

Reaction of magnesium and its compounds with acid

You need to know about the reactions of Mg, MgO, $Mg(OH)_2$ and $MgCO_3$ with dilute hydrochloric acid.

Thermal stability of group 2 nitrates and carbonates

What is this trend and how can it be explained?

It becomes harder to decompose the nitrates and carbonates as you go down the group; this is because the polarizing ability of the metal ion decreases as you go down the group, due to the decrease in charge density of the cation.

THE JARGON
As you go down the group, the ionic radius increases, so the +2 charge is spread over a greater volume. We say the charge density has decreased.

Carbonates decompose to the oxide and carbon dioxide.
Nitrates decompose to NO_2 and O_2.

LINKS
The thermal stabilities of group 2 nitrates and carbonates show the same trend as those of group 1, as shown on p. 39.

Solubility trends of the hydroxides and sulphates

Are these statements true or false? If they are false, explain why.

As you go down group 2, the solubility of the hydroxide decreases	False solubility goes up
As you go down group 2, the solubility of the sulphate decreases	True
Insolubility of $BaSO_4$ is used to identify Ba^{2+} ions and SO_4^{2-} ions	True
$Mg(OH)_2$ is not very soluble and does not form many OH^- ions in solution; $Ba(OH)_2$ is much more soluble and forms more OH^- ions in solution	True

Turn the page for some exam questions on this topic ➤

For more on this topic, see pages 90–91 of the *Revision Express A-level Study Guide*

Exam question 1

A student wanted to compare the reactivity of magnesium, calcium and strontium, so they reacted a small piece of each with oxygen, cold water and dilute hydrochloric acid. Complete this results table to say what would have occurred.

DON'T FORGET
Write down all the things you would *see*. Give the identity of any gases formed.

	Held in Bunsen flame	Reaction dropped in cold water	Reaction dropped in acid
Mg	Bright white flame White solid formed	No reaction	Vigorous Mg dissolves $H_{2(g)}$ formed
Ca	Brick red flame White solid formed	Fairly vigorous Ca dissolves $H_{2(g)}$ formed	Very vigorous Ca dissolves $H_{2(g)}$ formed
Sr	Crimson flame White solid formed	Vigorous Sr dissolves $H_{2(g)}$ formed	Extremely vigorous Sr dissolves $H_{2(g)}$ formed

Exam question 2

The trends in behaviour of group 2 metals and their compounds can be explained using a few core ideas A, B, C. As you go down the group:

A the outer electron configuration is always s^2
B the distance of the outer electron from the nucleus increases
C the charge density on the cation decreases

For each of these five trends, say whether A, B or C is responsible.

DON'T FORGET
There is one trend you do not have to explain, the trend in the solubilities of the hydroxides and sulphates.

The reactivity increases as you go down the group	B
The thermal stability of nitrates and carbonates increases as you go down the group	C
They all show a +2 oxidation state	A
Decrease in first ionization energy	B
Decrease in melting point of the oxides from MgO to BaO	C

Exam question 3

$Mg(NO_3)_2$ and $MgCO_3$ decompose relatively easily on heating. Write balanced equations, with state symbols, to show this.

DON'T FORGET
You've probably done this in the laboratory; think back over what happened and it may help you write the equations.

$$2Mg(NO_3)_{2(s)} \rightarrow 2MgO_{(s)} + 4NO_{2(g)} + O_{2(g)}$$

$$MgCO_{3(s)} \rightarrow MgO_{(s)} + CO_{2(g)}$$

AS OCR WJEC

Limestone – calcium carbonate

Calcium carbonate gives us the warm yellow of a Cotswold limestone and the white cliffs of Dover, but it's got much more than just a pretty face.

Decomposition of limestone

This process has been carried out for centuries in limekilns and cement works throughout the world. The $CaCO_3$ is heated strongly to bring about its decomposition.

For each of these processes, write in the product name, its formula and its state.

Process	Product	Trivial name	Formula and state
Heating $CaCO_3$	calcium oxide	quicklime	$CaO_{(s)}$
Adding water to quicklime	calcium hydroxide	slaked lime	$Ca(OH)_{2(s)}$
Dissolving the quicklime completely	calcium hydroxide	limewater solution	$Ca(OH)_{2(aq)}$

Reactions of limewater

Limewater is the test for carbon dioxide gas, but how does it work? Calcium hydroxide solution has a pH of about 11 and will absorb acidic gases such as CO_2. In doing so, it goes milky as solid $CaCO_3$ forms, but if excess CO_2 is passed through, it becomes clear again as the $CaCO_3$ redissolves to form calcium hydrogencarbonate.

Complete these word and symbol equations.

calcium hydroxide + carbon dioxide → calcium carbonate + water

$$Ca(OH)_{2(aq)} + CO_{2(g)} \rightarrow CaCO_{3(s)} + H_2O_{(l)}$$

calcium carbonate + carbon dioxide + water → calcium hydrogencarbonate

$$CaCO_{3(s)} + CO_{2(s)} + H_2O_{(l)} \rightarrow Ca(HCO_3)_{2(aq)}$$

This last reaction is what causes caves to form in limestone regions. Rain, with dissolved carbon dioxide, dissolves the limestone and carries it away as a solution of calcium hydrogencarbonate.

What happens when you boil water with Ca^{2+} ions in it?

When water containing Ca^{2+} ions is boiled, calcium carbonate will be precipitated. This is known as hard water and it leaves scale or fur in pipes, boilers and kettles.

Turn the page for some exam questions on this topic ➤

For more on this topic, see pages 91–92 of the *Revision Express A-level Study Guide*

Exam question 1

The compounds of group 2 elements are put to various uses. For each of the compounds listed below, give a use and explain the chemistry behind it.

THE JARGON
A suspension is a mixture of liquid and tiny particles of solid, which remain suspended rather than settling out quickly.

	Use	Chemistry behind use
Magnesium hydroxide suspension	Ingredient in antacid medicines	$Mg(OH)_2$ is a base, so it neutralizes acids without forming gas
Calcium carbonate	Removes acidity in lake waters	Cheap slow-release neutralization of acids in lakes
Aqueous calcium hydroxide	Limewater	Reacts with CO_2 to form insoluble $CaCO_3$
Solid calcium hydroxide	To remove acidity in soil	Quick-acting base neutralizes acids

Exam question 2

Some data books on analysis write the following:

Ion	Test. Add NaOH, first dropwise then to excess
Ba^{2+}	No precipitate provided reagents are pure

A technician makes up the solutions from 100% pure $BaCl_2$ and deionized water before a practical exam and uses the NaOH solution from the reagent cupboard, but they cannot get the test to behave as it should. The solution keeps going cloudy. Using your knowledge of the group 2 solubility trend, see if you can help them.

Is barium hydroxide soluble?

$Ba(OH)_2$ is soluble, hence it shouldn't give a ppt.

If the NaOH solution is not completely fresh, is there anything it might have reacted with?

Alkaline NaOH will react with acidic CO_2 in the air.

When the NaOH reacts with CO_2, what solution does it form?

You often see a white crust of this around the tops of NaOH bottles that haven't been used for a while.

It forms sodium carbonate solution.

Suggest an identity for the technician's precipitate and write an ionic equation for its formation.

Use what you know about the trend in solubilities of the sulphates and assume this holds for the carbonates.

Some barium carbonate forms:

$$Ba^{2+}_{(aq)} + CO^{2-}_{3(aq)} \rightarrow BaCO_{3(s)}$$

AS OCR Edexcel AQA WJEC CCEA

The behaviour of group 7 – the halogens

The halogens are all non-metals and they show clear trends in their physical and chemical behaviour.

Trend in volatility

This graph shows how the boiling points of the halogens vary. Explain the variation in boiling point shown by the halogens.

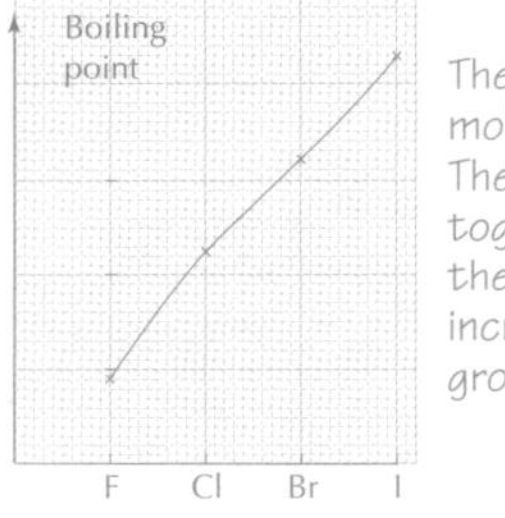

The halogens exist as diatomic molecules with no permanent dipole. The only forces holding molecules together are van der Waals forces; they increase in strength with the increased number of electrons as the group is descended.

THE JARGON
Volatility describes the ease with which a substance forms a vapour.

Displacement reactions

As you go down the group, the reactivity of the halogens decreases.

Complete these ionic equations to show displacement reactions of the halogens. If no reaction occurs, write 'no reaction'.

$Cl_{2(g)} + 2Br^-_{(aq)} \rightarrow 2Cl^-_{(aq)} + Br_{2(aq)}$

$Br_{2(aq)} + 2Cl^-_{(aq)} \rightarrow$ no reaction

$Br_{2(aq)} + 2I^-_{(aq)} \rightarrow 2Br^-_{(aq)} + I_{2(aq)}$

$I_{2(aq)} + 2Cl^-_{(aq)} \rightarrow$ no reaction

SYLLABUS CHECK
Displacement by chlorine is mentioned by Edexcel as a means of obtaining bromine from seawater.

Tick which of these explanations correctly explains the statement. If it is incorrect explain why.

Correct statement	Explanation	
The halide ions show an oxidation number of −1 in their compounds with metals	Their outer electron arrangement is s^2p^5 and they gain one electron from metals when they react	✔
Hydrogen halide solutions are acidic	When they dissolve in water they release OH^- ions	No, they release H^+ ions
Chlorine is a better oxidizing agent than bromine	Chlorine can gain electrons more readily than bromine	✔
When concentrated sulphuric acid is added to solid halides, sodium chloride releases HCl but sodium iodide releases I_2	An iodide ion is less easily oxidized than a chloride ion	No, I^- is easier to oxidize
Iodide ions are better reducing agents than chloride ions	Iodide ions more readily lose electrons than chloride ions	✔

SPEED LEARNING
OILRIG: oxidation is loss of electrons, reduction is gain of electrons.

DON'T FORGET
A good oxidizing agent will always be easily reduced.

Turn the page for some exam questions on this topic ➤

For more on this topic, see pages 108–111 of the *Revision Express A-level Study Guide*

Exam question 1

A student has three solutions, P, Q and R, which they know are halides. First they are given silver nitrate solution and dilute ammonia solution. Describe how they would carry out a test to distinguish them and state what they would observe with each halide.

What test would they do?

Add a few drops of silver nitrate solution followed by an excess of ammonia solution.

Complete the table.

Halide present	Observation
Cl^-	White ppt. forms which dissolves readily in ammonia solution
Br^-	Cream ppt. forms which dissolves partially in ammonia solution
I^-	Yellow ppt. forms which does not dissolve in ammonia solution

THE JARGON
ppt. is short for precipitate. This is when two solutions are added and a solid forms.

Next the student is told to identify solutions P, Q and R by using solutions of Cl_2, Br_2 and I_2. Unfortunately, the label has fallen off the solutions of Cl_2 and I_2. Using only litmus paper, how could they distinguish the solutions of Cl_2 and I_2?

The Cl_2 solution will quickly bleach litmus paper, whereas the I_2 solution has no bleaching effect.

Now the student has positively identified each halogen solution, they carry out the following tests with the following results. Read these results then identify each solution explaining your reasoning.

Test carried out	Result
1 Cl_2 water mixed with each halide solution in turn	P and Q became darker R did not change
2 Starch solution added to solutions from test 1	Q immediately turned blue-black P and R did not change

Start with R.

R is $Cl^-_{(aq)}$ since no reaction occurred with $Cl_{2(aq)}$.

Now distinguish between P and Q.

P and Q are $Br^-_{(aq)}$ and $I^-_{(aq)}$. When $Cl_{2(aq)}$ is bubbled through, the halogen is displaced. Cl_2 oxidizes $Br^-_{(aq)}$ to $Br_{2(aq)}$ and $I^-_{(aq)}$ to $I_{2(aq)}$.

Starch is a test for iodine, which forms a blue-black complex with it. So Q is $I^-_{(aq)}$ and P is $Br^-_{(aq)}$.

Reactions of group 7

Here we look at some reactions of group 7 that hinge around redox reactions.

Halides with concentrated sulphuric acid

The reducing ability of halide ions increases down the group. This is seen when concentrated sulphuric acid is added to a solid halide.

Complete the conclusion column.

Observation when concentrated sulphuric acid is added to the solid halide	Conclusion Halide ion present
A brown gas forms which turns damp blue litmus paper red	Br_2 gas Br^- present
Violet vapour forms immediately	I_2 gas I^- present
Gas formed which turns damp blue litmus paper red but does not bleach it. It forms white clouds with NH_3 gas	HCl gas Cl^- present

Reaction of Cl_2 with water

Chlorine disproportionates when it reacts with water, forming the chloride ion and chloric(I) acid.

Add the oxidation states above chlorine and then add labelled arrows to show the disproportionation.

reduction, oxidation

0 −1 +1

$$Cl_{2(g)} + H_2O_{(l)} \rightarrow Cl^-_{(aq)} + HClO_{(aq)} + H^+_{(aq)}$$

THE JARGON
Disproportionation occurs when a substance is simultaneously oxidized and reduced.

Chlorine is used in this way in water sterilization. The chloric(I) acid is a strong oxidizing agent and kills bacteria.

Reaction of Cl_2 with sodium hydroxide

Only two of these equations are correct and are correctly described in terms of redox. Put a tick beside them.

Equation	Description	
$Cl_2 + 2NaOH \rightarrow NaCl + NaClO + H_2$	Cold; Cl oxidized only	
$3NaClO \rightarrow NaCl + NaClO_3$	Cold; Cl disproportionates	
$Cl_2 + 2NaOH \rightarrow NaCl + NaClO + H_2$	Hot; Cl disproportionates	
$3NaClO \rightarrow 2NaCl + NaClO_3$	Hot; Cl disproportionates	✔
$Cl_2 + 2NaOH \rightarrow 2NaCl + NaClO + H_2$	Cold; Cl disproportionates	✔
$3NaClO \rightarrow NaCl + NaClO_3$	Hot; Cl reduced only	

SYLLABUS CHECK
Only Edexcel and CCEA require the reaction with hot NaOH to make chlorate(V).

You need to learn the two correct equations and their descriptions. One of these is the reaction that the membrane cell is designed to avoid.

LINKS
To see how the membrane cell works, have a look at p. 49.

Turn the page for some exam questions on this topic ➤

For more on this topic, see pages 108–111 of the *Revision Express A-level Study Guide*

Exam question 1

Household bleaches often contain sodium chlorate(I). A student wants to find the concentration of this in a commercially available bleach. They have carried out an experiment to estimate the amount of ClO^- in each, using the fact that it will release iodine when reacted with potassium iodide solution. The amount of iodine released can then be found by performing a titration with a standard solution of sodium thiosulphate. Here are the half-equations for these reactions:

$$ClO^-_{(aq)} + 2H^+_{(aq)} + 2e^- \rightarrow C^-_{(aq)} + H_2O_{(l)}$$

$$I_{2(aq)} + 2e^- \rightarrow 2I^-_{(aq)}$$

$$S_4O_6^{2-}{}_{(aq)} + 2e^- \rightarrow 2S_2O_3^{2-}{}_{(aq)}$$

DON'T FORGET
When combining a pair of half-equations, one is written as a forward reaction and the other as the reverse reaction. When they're added together, the electrons cancel out.

Use the half-equations to write a balanced equation for each reaction.

$ClO^-_{(aq)} + 2I^-_{(aq)} + 2H^+_{(aq)} \rightarrow ClO^-_{(aq)} + H_2O_{(l)} + I_{2(aq)}$

$2S_2O^{2-}_{3(aq)} + I_{2(aq)} \rightarrow S_4O^{2-}_{6(aq)} + 2I^-_{(aq)}$

What indicator would be used and what would happen at the endpoint?

Starch is used as an indicator. At the endpoint it turns from blue-black to colourless.

For each bleach, 5.0 cm³ were placed into a 100 cm³ volumetric flask, which was then topped up with deionized water. A 10.0 cm³ sample of bleach A was removed and reacted with an excess of acidified potassium iodide solution. The resulting iodine needed 15.00 cm³ of 0.10 mol dm⁻³ sodium thiosulphate to react fully. Calculate the concentration of ClO^- in bleach A.

Calculate the number of moles of thiosulphate used in the titration.

$n = cv = 15.00/1\,000 \times 0.10$

$= 1.50 \times 10^{-3}$ mol thiosulphate

From the equations, find the ratio of $S_2O_3^{2-}$, I_2 and ClO^- in order to find the number of moles of ClO^- in the 10.0 cm³ sample.

$S_2O_3^{2-} : I_2 : ClO^-$

2 : 1 : 1

How much ClO^- was in the volumetric flask in total?

There was 7.50×10^{-4} mol of ClO^- in the 10.0 cm³ sample

The flask contained 100 cm³ of solution, so there was 7.50×10^{-3} mol of ClO^- in the flask

What was the concentration of the original bleach?

All of this came from the original 5.0 cm³ of bleach, so using the formula $n = cv$ we have

$c = n / v$
$= 7.50 \times 10^{-3}/5.0 \times 10^{-3}$
$= 1.5$ mol dm^{-3}

Industrial extractions

AS Edexcel AQA WJEC CCEA

This section looks at four important industrial processes. Look carefully at the syllabus checks.

SYLLABUS CHECK
AQA only for iron extraction.

Extracting iron

Iron is extracted in a high-temperature continuous process in a blast furnace; the raw materials are

Name the raw materials.

iron ore, coke, limestone, air

Coke burns to form CO_2 exothermically; this heats the furnace:

Write the equation here.

$C_{(s)} + O_{2(g)} \rightarrow CO_{2(g)}$

The CO_2 then reacts with more carbon:

Write the equation here.

$C_{(s)} + CO_{2\,(g)} \rightarrow 2CO_{(g)}$

Both CO and C can act as reducing agents in different parts of the furnace but the main reducing agent is CO:

Write two equations to show reduction of iron oxide by C and by CO.

$3C_{(s)} + 2\,Fe_2O_{3(s)} \rightarrow 3CO_{2(g)} + 4Fe_{(l)}$

$3CO_{(g)} + Fe_2O_{3(s)} \rightarrow 3CO_{2(g)} + 2Fe_{(l)}$

Limestone ($CaCO_3$) is added to remove sandy impurities as liquid slag. It decomposes into CaO; the CaO reacts to remove SiO_2:

Write an equation for SiO_2 removal.

$CaO_{(s)} + SiO_{2(s)} \rightarrow CaSiO_{3(l)}$

Other wastes are oxides of carbon and, if sulphide ores are used, sulphur dioxide gas.

SYLLABUS CHECK
Edexcel requires you to know principles of the membrane cell.

Electrolysis of brine

Put these labels onto the diagram of the membrane cell in the correct place: chlorine, hydrogen, $Na^+_{(aq)}$ moves through, anode, cathode, brine in, spent brine out, dil. $NaOH_{(aq)}$ in, conc. $NaOH_{(aq)}$ out.

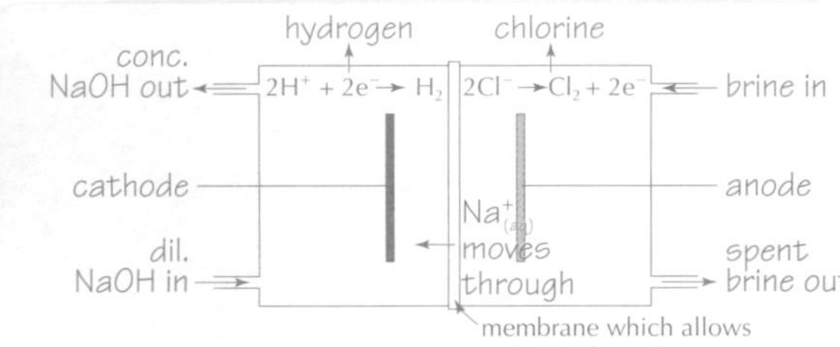

SYLLABUS CHECK
AQA only.

Extraction of titanium

Titanium is the ninth most abundant element in the Earth's crust but it is very expensive. This is down to the high costs of extraction.

Shade in three different colours to link the process in the first column, the equation in the second and the comment in the third. The first column shows the processes in the correct order.

First titanium oxide is converted to its chloride	$TiCl_{4(l)} + 2Mg_{(l)} \rightarrow Ti_{(s)} + 2MgCl_{2(l)}$	At 700 °C under an inert Ar atmosphere
Then titanium chloride is reduced using Mg or Na	$TiO_{2(s)} + 2Cl_{2(g)} + 2C_{(s)} \rightarrow TiCl_{4(l)} + 2CO_{(g)}$	Electrolysis
Mg is reclaimed from the $MgCl_2$ so it can be used again	$MgCl_{2(l)} \rightarrow Mg_{(l)} + Cl_{2(g)}$	Heating with carbon and chlorine

Turn the page for some exam questions on this topic ➤

For more on this topic, see pages 93, 112 of the *Revision Express A-level Study Guide*

SYLLABUS CHECK
Question 1 for Edexcel only but question 2 for all exam boards.

Exam question 1

This question concerns the extraction of aluminium from its ore, bauxite.

(a) Outline the purification of aluminium oxide; include an explanation of the chemistry involved. Equations are not required for the purification.

(b) Outline the electrolysis of aluminium oxide. Give equations for the electrode reactions and state and explain the conditions used.

The statements explain how the aluminium oxide is purified. Number the statements to get them in the right order.

This means that the impurities can be filtered off	4
Aluminium oxide is amphoteric and dissolves in NaOH solution	2
The impurities are insoluble in NaOH solution	3
The solution after filtration contains the aluminate ion	5
A small amount of pure aluminium oxide is added, which causes precipitation of the oxide	6
Bauxite is Al_2O_3 with impurities like iron oxide and silica	1

THE JARGON
Amphoteric means that it will react with both acids and alkalis.

What ions are present in aluminium oxide?

First the pure oxide must be made molten but the melting point is 2045 °C. Why is it so high and how is it lowered?

Al^{3+} and O^{2-} ions are present. The bonding is ionic and the ions are both small and highly charged so they are strongly attracted. By mixing with cryolite, Na_3AlF_6, the melting point is lowered to 950 °C.

What occurs at the cathode?

Reduction occurs at the cathode:

$Al^{3+}_{(l)} + 3e^- \rightarrow Al_{(l)}$

What occurs at the anode?

Oxidation occurs at the anode:

$2O^{2-}_{(g)} \rightarrow O_{2(g)} + 4e^-$

This is unfortunate for the carbon anode. Why is that?

It burns away in the ready supply of oxygen.

Exam question 2

If 102 kg of Al_2O_3 are electrolysed, what mass of Al and what volume of O_2, measured at STP, would be formed? (Al = 27, O = 16)

Calculate moles of Al_2O_3 then write a balanced equation.

$n = m / M_r = 102\,000/102 = 1\,000$ moles Al_2O_3

$2Al_2O_3 \rightarrow 4\,Al + 3O_2$

How many moles of Al come from 1 mole of Al_2O_3?

2 mol $2Al_2O_3 \rightarrow$ 4 mol Al

1 mol $Al_2O_3 \rightarrow$ 2 mol Al

How many kilograms of Al form?

1 000 mol $Al_2O_3 \rightarrow$ 2 000 mol Al

$m = nM_r = 2\,000 \times 27$

$= 54\,000$g or **54 kg Al**

What volume of O_2 forms?

2 mol $Al_2O_3 \rightarrow$ 3 mol O_2; 1 000 mol $\rightarrow$ 1 500 mol

1 mol O_2 at STP = 22.4 dm^3

1 500 mol = **33 600 dm^3**

DON'T FORGET
1 mole of any gas at STP occupies 22.4 dm^3.

Organic chemistry – the basics

This section introduces some of the basic ideas that you need for the rest of the book.

Different types of formula

Draw the example in the third column using the rules in the second.

General formula of alkanes	Used to represent any member of a homologous series (see below)	C_nH_{2n+2}
Molecular formula of ethanol	Shows the number of each type of atom in the compound	C_2H_6O
Structural formula of ethanol	The minimal amount of detail that allows an unambiguous formula to be worked out	CH_3CH_2OH
Displayed formula of ethanoic acid	Shows the relative placing and number of bonds between atoms	H–C(H)(H)–C(=O)–O–H
Skeletal formula of butane	Hydrogen atoms are removed to leave a carbon skeleton and functional groups	

Three terms are defined: nomenclature, functional group, homologous series. Write the correct term beside its definition.

Homologous series	A series of compounds with the same functional group where each member increases by $-CH_2-$ and which can be described by a general formula
Nomenclature	A system of naming compounds. You should use IUPAC rules
Functional group	The part of a molecule that dictates its chemical behaviour

THE JARGON
IUPAC stands for International Union of Pure and Applied Chemistry.

Types of reaction

Beside each description, state the type of reaction. Choose your answers from these words: hydrolysis, elimination, oxidation, electrophilic, free, radical, addition, nucleophilic, substitution, reduction.

Free radical	Where attack is by a species with an unpaired electron
Addition	Two species add to each other
Substitution	Swapping one species for another
Elimination	One species breaks down to two
Hydrolysis	When water breaks open a bond
Reduction	Gain of hydrogen or loss of oxygen
Oxidation	Gain of oxygen or loss of hydrogen
Electrophilic	Where the reagent is attracted by negative charge in the target molecule
Nucleophilic	Where the reagent is attracted by positive charge in the target molecule

Turn the page for some exam questions on this topic ➤

For more on this topic, see pages 140–145 of the *Revision Express A-level Study Guide*

Exam question 1

LINKS
You may need to look at p. 59 in order to answer these questions.

This question concerns the linear molecule, C_4H_8.

What functional group does it contain?

C_4H_8 contains a double bond (alkene group)

What is its general formula?

C_nH_{2n} is the general formula for alkenes

What is the next member of this homologous series?

C_5H_{10} is the next member of this series

Draw displayed formulae for two straight-chain structural isomers of C_4H_8 and name them.

THE JARGON
Structural isomerism occurs when compounds have the same molecular formula but different structural formulae.

$H_2C=CH-CH_2-CH_3$ — but-1-ene

$H_3C-CH=CH-CH_3$ — but-2-ene

Draw the displayed formula for another structural isomer of C_4H_8 that does not show *cis / trans* isomerism and explain why it doesn't.

THE JARGON
In alkenes, *cis / trans* isomerism occurs when there is at least one double bond in a molecule. There must be two different groups attached at either end of the double bond.

$H_2C=C(CH_3)_2$

It does not have two different species at either end of the double bond, so no *cis / trans* isomerism.

Draw and name the *cis / trans* isomers of but-2-ene.

cis form: H and H on the same side, CH_3 and CH_3 on the same side of C=C

trans form: CH_3 and H on each carbon, opposite sides of C=C

Alkanes

AS OCR Edexcel AQA WJEC CCEA

The simplest of organic compounds, the alkanes are saturated hydrocarbons and show very limited chemistry.

Why are alkanes so unreactive?

All these statements are true. Tick the two statements that together explain the unreactivity of alkanes.

1. All alkanes contain strong covalent bonds ☐
2. The covalent bonds are not at all polar because the electronegativity of C and H is so similar ☑
3. Van der Waals' forces are stronger when molecules can approach more closely ☐
4. Van der Waals forces become larger as the number of electrons increases ☐
5. There are only van der Waals forces holding individual molecules together ☐
6. Alkanes do not attract nucleophiles or electrophiles ☑

What property is explained by statement 5? Which statement explains why the boiling point of alkanes increases with increased chain length? Which one explains why branched alkanes have lower boiling points than their straight-chain counterparts?

Statement 5 explains their low boiling points. Statement 4 explains why boiling point increases with chain length. Statement 3 explains why branched alkanes have lower boiling points than their straight-chain isomers.

Alkanes have two main types of reaction. What are they?

Combustion and free radical substitution

SYLLABUS CHECK
Edexcel does not require any mechanisms.

Mechanism of free radical substitution

INITIATION

Chlorine molecules absorb energy from ultraviolet light and undergo homolytic fission:

Write the equation.

$$Cl_2 \rightarrow 2Cl\cdot$$

THE JARGON
Homolytic fission is when the single bond is broken and one electron goes onto each chlorine, forming two free radicals $Cl\cdot$.

PROPAGATION

The chlorine free radical attacks methane, pulling off a hydrogen and its electron and leaving a methyl free radical:

Write the equation.

$$Cl\cdot + CH_4 \rightarrow HCl + CH_3\cdot$$

The free radical is regenerated when the $CH_3\cdot$ free radical attacks another chlorine molecule:

Write the equation.

$$CH_3\cdot + Cl_2 \rightarrow CH_3Cl + Cl\cdot$$

The propagation steps repeat many times, only stopping when termination occurs.

TERMINATION

Two free radicals combine to form a molecule, e.g.

Write the equation.

$$CH_3\cdot + Cl\cdot \rightarrow CH_3Cl$$

Turn the page for some exam questions on this topic ➤

For more on this topic, see page 146 of the *Revision Express A-level Study Guide*

SYLLABUS CHECK
Edexcel does not require any mechanisms.

Exam question 1

The photochlorination of methane by a free radical mechanism can lead to the formation of CH_2Cl_2 and CCl_4. Draw out a sequence of steps that show how CH_2Cl_2 could form, starting with Cl_2 and CH_4.

Initiation

$$Cl_2 \rightarrow 2Cl\cdot$$

Propagation

$$Cl\cdot + CH_4 \rightarrow HCl + CH_3\cdot$$

$$CH_3\cdot + Cl_2 \rightarrow Cl\cdot + CH_3Cl$$

$$Cl\cdot + CH_3Cl \rightarrow CH_2Cl\cdot + HCl$$

Termination

$$CH_2Cl\cdot + Cl\cdot \rightarrow CH_2Cl_2$$

Exam question 2

Methane, propane and butane are all used as fuels around the house and garden. Write equations for the complete combustion of all three and say why these reactions are exothermic.

$$CH_4 + O_2 \rightarrow CO_2 + 2\,H_2O$$

$$C_3H_8 + 5O_2 \rightarrow 3CO_2 + 4H_2O$$

$$2C_4H_{10} + 13O_2 \rightarrow 8CO_2 + 10H_2O$$

These are all exothermic because more energy is given out by forming bonds than is taken in by breaking them. The C=O bond is very strong.

LINKS
For a reminder of bond energies, see p. 22.

Exam question 3

A sample of an alkane undergoes complete combustion. The products were collected at RTP and were found to be 1.44 dm³ of CO_2 and 1.26 g of water. Calculate the empirical formula of the alkane. (C = 12, H = 1.0, O = 16)

LINKS
For information on the volume of 1 mole of gas at RTP, see p. 7

Calculate moles of H_2O and hence H.

$n = m / M_r = 1.26/18 = 0.07$ mol $H_2O = 0.14$ mol H
1 mole = 24 dm³ at RTP

Caculate moles of CO_2 and hence C.

so we have 1.44/24 = 0.06 mol CO_2
= 0.06 mol C

Find simplest ratio of these.

Ratio C:H = 0.06:0.14 = 3:7
so empirical formula is C_3H_7

If M_r = 86, what is the molecular formula?

C_3H_7 has M_r = 43, so there are two lots of it in the molecular formula, which must be C_6H_{14}

AS OCR AQA WJEC CCEA

Making the most of crude oil

The source of hydrocarbons is crude oil but this must be processed before anything useful can be done with it.

SYLLABUS CHECK
OCR and AQA cover this topic in rather more depth than other syllabuses; check yours to see what you can miss out.

Fractional distillation

This is the first process carried out on crude oil. The mixture of hydrocarbons is heated and fractions are separated depending on the size of the carbon chain.

Why does this process work?

The length of the carbon chain determines the size of the van der Waals forces holding the molecules together, which in turn controls the boiling point.

Cracking

After fractional distillation the volume of each product obtained does not match the demand for it. Cracking breaks larger molecules into smaller ones, which are more in demand. This requires high temperature and pressure and it occurs by a free radical mechanism.

What else is obtained by cracking?

Alkenes are always obtained during cracking.

Thermal cracking produces a large proportion of alkenes

If C_9H_{20} is cracked and one of the two products is C_6H_{14}, write a balanced equation for the reaction; name both products.

$C_9H_{20} \rightarrow C_6H_{14} + C_3H_6$
hexane propene

Why are such high temperatures required?

High temperatures are needed because C–C bonds must be broken and this means there will be a high activation energy.

If this is a free radical mechanism, will it be homolytic or heterolytic bond fission?

To make a free radical, the fission must be homolytic since this gives species with unpaired electrons. Once formed, these free radicals attack the long-chain hydrocarbons, creating a large number of different products.

THE JARGON
Zeolites are a group of minerals. They are used in ion exchange columns, for water purification.

Catalytic cracking

If cracking is carried out with a zeolite catalyst, at fairly high temperatures but lower pressures, the products contain a higher proportion of cycloalkanes and arenes. These are desirable for the most efficient burning of petrol.

Isomerization and reforming

Alternatively, two other processes are carried out to convert straight-chain alkanes: isomerization and reforming.

Read the descriptions and write in the name beside each process.

Isomerization	Straight-chain compounds are converted to branched-chain compounds
reforming	Conversion to cycloalkanes and arenes

Turn the page for some exam questions on this topic ➤

For more on this topic, see page 164 of the *Revision Express A-level Study Guide*

Exam question 1

Fractional distillation is the first process in refining crude oil. Read the questions in the margin then answer in the spaces provided.

The diagram shows a fractionating column. What property of the hydrocarbons allows them to be separated in this way?

The molecules can be separated because

they have different boiling points; low boiling point fractions rise to the top of the tower; high boiling point products remain nearer the base

Label the missing fractions.

Label the number of carbon atoms present in molecules of the petrol fraction.

gases
<40°C
petrol
5–10°C
naphtha
kerosene
gas oil
fuel oil
crude oil
350°–400°C
bitumen

Cracking may be carried out on the alkanes obtained from fractional distillation. Why is this necessary?

Cracking is necessary because

the demand for long-chain alkanes present in the crude oil is low and that for smaller-chain alkanes and alkenes is high

Octane ratings for petrol are based on the combustion of the branched-chain alkane 2,2,4-trimethylpentane being set at 100. Branched alkanes like this burn in a more controlled fashion. Draw this molecule.

2,2,4-trimethylpentane

```
   H  CH3  H  CH3  H
   |   |   |   |   |
H—C — C — C — C — C—H
   |   |   |   |   |
   H  CH3  H   H   H
```

Two processes

Name two processes that could be carried out on a long-chain alkane in order to obtain more branched products.

Isomerization and catalytic cracking

Alternatives to oil

Oil reserves are finite. What alternatives are there for fuel production?

Biofuels are the most promising alternative

Various pollutants are produced during combustion of hydrocarbon fuels, namely CO_2, SO_2, NO_x, CO. Complete this table to show the gases and their effects.

Cause	Pollutant gas	Effect
Sulphur present as impurities	SO_2	acid rain
Complete combustion of carbon in the fuel	CO_2	greenhouse effect global warming
Incomplete combustion of fuel	CO	poisonous
High temperature and pressure in the petrol engine	NO_x	smog and acid rain

THE JARGON
NO_x is a general formula to show a variety of nitrogen oxides.

AS OCR Edexcel AQA WJEC CCEA

Alkenes

Alkenes are unsaturated hydrocarbons whose double bond makes them attractive to electrophiles, causing them to be much more reactive than alkanes.

Bonding in alkenes

Molecular orbitals form when atoms share their electrons.

Draw the shape of s and p atomic orbitals and label them.

s orbital p orbital

Sigma bonds (σ bonds) form when atomic orbitals combine to form molecular orbitals by **end-on-end** overlap.

Show the formation of a sigma bond from the overlap of a p orbital and an s orbital.

sigma bond

This is the type of bond we see in ethane. But in ethene, something different happens. Adjacent p orbitals overlap **sideways** and form pi molecular orbitals (π molecular orbitals).

The shape of an ethene molecule

Draw a molecule of ethene showing all of the σ and π bonds in it.

π bond H H C C H H π bond ○ = σ bond

In one word describe its shape.

planar

Addition reactions of ethene

The table shows addition reactions of ethene as a typical alkene. Complete the products column.

Reactants	Product	Comments
Hydrogen	ethane	Ni catalyst at 200 °C
Bromine	1,2-dibromoethane	Br_2 is decolorized; the test for an alkene
HI	iodoethane	Quick at room temperature
Steam	ethanol	Catalyst H_3PO_4 at 300 °C and 70 atm
H_2SO_4	ethyl hydrogen sulphate; further reaction with H_2O gives ethanol	Concentrated acid; slow at room temperature
Ethene	poly(ethene)	LDPE in extreme conditions; HDPE in moderate conditions and with catalyst
$KMnO_4$	ethane-1,2-diol	Acidified MnO_4^- is decolorized; this is not addition but oxidation

SYLLABUS CHECK
Check your syllabus to see which of these reactions you need and tick them now.

IF YOU HAVE TIME
Practice writing equations for the reactions on your syllabus.

THE JARGON
LDPE is low-density poly(ethene); HDPE is high-density poly(ethene).

Turn the page for some exam questions on this topic ➤

For more on this topic, see pages 147–148 of the *Revision Express A-level Study Guide*

Exam question 1

This question is about propene. Draw displayed formulae and name the products when propene is reacted with the reagents shown.

Reaction with H_2 / Ni.

H_2 / Ni → propane

```
  H H H
  | | |
H-C-C-C-H
  | | |
  H H H
```

Steam / H_3PO_4.

Steam / H_3PO_4 → propan-2-ol

```
  H H  H
  | |  |
H-C-C--C-H
  | |  |
  H OH H
```

Two possible isomers from the reaction with HBr.

HBr →

```
  H Br H            H H H
  | |  |            | | |
H-C-C--C-H        H-C-C-C-Br
  | |  |            | | |
  H H  H            H H H
```

2-bromopropane 1-bromopropane

Exam question 2

SYLLABUS CHECK
AQA only.

Epoxyethane, a very reactive molecule, is used for making other substances like polyesters and ethane-1,2-diol (antifreeze). Draw a diagram of epoxyethane and explain why it is so reactive.

```
H   O   H
 \ / \ /
  C - C
 /     \
H       H
```

The three-membered ring is very strained; this makes it a reactive molecule.

How is epoxyethane made from ethene?

What are the hazards involved in this process?

Ethene is reacted directly with oxygen at 250 °C in the presence of a silver catalyst.

Epoxyethane is toxic and explosive.

Epoxyethane can be reacted to make ethane-1,2-diol. Draw a displayed formula for ethane-1,2-diol.

```
   H  H
   |  |
H—C——C—H
   |  |
  OH  OH
```

Epoxyethane can be reacted with alcohols. What are the products used for?

The products are used for manufacturing surfactants, plasticizers and solvents.

AS OCR AQA WJEC CCEA

Reaction mechanisms for alkenes

As well as knowing the reactions of alkenes you also need to be able to recall their mechanisms.

SYLLABUS CHECK
Edexcel does not require details of mechanisms at AS.

Mechanism of the reaction between ethene and bromine

Consider the mechanism for the reaction between ethene and bromine. As you read through the stages, you need to add various items to the diagram.

Stage 1

The bromine molecule approaches the ethene. The high density of the electrons of the pi bond of ethene causes the bromine to become polarized.

Draw the dipole that will form on bromine.

$H_2C{=}CH_2 \quad Br^{\delta+}{-}Br^{\delta-}$

Stage 2

The C=C bond breaks by heterolytic fission. The bromine molecule acts as an electron pair acceptor – an electrophile. At the same time, heterolytic fission of the Br–Br bond occurs and the electron pair moves onto the other bromine atom.

Draw curly arrows to show the movement of electrons out of the double bond onto bromine and the movement of the electron pair out of the Br–Br bond.

$H_2C{=}CH_2 \quad Br^{\delta+}{-}Br^{\delta-}$

THE JARGON
A curly arrow shows the movement of a pair of electrons.

Stage 3

An unstable intermediate forms in which one carbon is electron deficient and so carries a positive charge. This is a carbocation, sometimes called a carbonium ion. A bromide ion is in the wings.

Draw the charge onto the carbocation and add a curly arrow to show the movement of the electron pair from the Br⁻ ion onto the positively charged carbon. Draw the product that forms and name it.

$H{-}CH(Br){-}\overset{+}{C}H_2 + Br^- \rightarrow H{-}CH(Br){-}CH(Br){-}H$

How would you classify this reaction?

The mechanism is electrophilic addition and the product is 1,2-dibromoethane.

Turn the page for some exam questions on this topic ➤

For more on this topic, see pages 144, 147 of the *Revision Express A-level Study Guide*

SYLLABUS CHECK
All syllabuses say that you should know about the possibility of two isomeric products, but AQA and WJEC specifically want this mechanism.

Exam question 1

When propene reacts with hydrogen bromide, there is a possibility of two isomers forming but one is always favoured over the other. By drawing out the mechanism, explain why this is the case. Name both possible products and identify the major product.

Using the molecule printed for you, draw the induced polarity on the HBr molecule and the curly arrow from the C=C bond.

$CH_3{-}CH{=}CH_2 \quad H^{\delta+}{-}Br^{\delta-}$

Now work in two columns for the two possibilities. At the top of column 1, add the H atom to the right-hand side of the bond and draw the + on the other carbon. Reverse this in column 2.

Alkyl groups have a positive inductive effect, pushing electrons onto the positively charged carbon. Show any such inductive effects with arrows along the bonds.

Notice that in column 1 there are two alkyl groups pushing electrons onto the carbocation. Label this secondary carbocation.

In column 2 there is only a single alkyl group stabilizing the carbocation. Label this primary carbocation.

Since the secondary carbocation is more stabilized, it is this one that will form the major product. Complete both columns and label the major product.

$CH_3{\rightarrow}\overset{+}{C}H{\leftarrow}CH_3$	$CH_3{-}CH_2{\rightarrow}\overset{+}{C}H_2$
Secondary carbocation	Primary carbocation
Two CH_3 groups push electrons onto the positively charged C, making it stable	Only one CH_3 group so the intermediate is not as stable as the secondary carbocation
$CH_3{-}CHBr{-}CH_3$	$CH_3{-}CH_2{-}CH_2Br$
2-bromopropane (major product)	1-bromopropane

SYLLABUS CHECK
AQA only.

Exam question 2

Draw the mechanism for the reaction of concentrated sulphuric acid with ethene. Show what happens when water is then added.

$H_2C{=}CH_2 + H^{\delta+}{-}O^{\delta-}SO_2OH \rightarrow H{-}CH_2{-}\overset{+}{C}H_2 + {}^-OSO_2OH \rightarrow H{-}CH_2{-}CH_2{-}OSO_3H$

$\xrightarrow{H_2O} H_2SO_4 + H{-}CH_2{-}CH_2{-}OH$

AS OCR Edexcel AQA WJEC CCEA

Uses of alkenes

The previous section reviewed some addition reactions of the alkenes. This section places them in an industrial context.

Hydrogenation of vegetable oils

This involves the addition of hydrogen across the double bonds in vegetable oil, causing it to harden and form margarine.

How is this done?

It is done by reacting the oil with hydrogen gas in the presence of a nickel catalyst.

Addition polymerization of ethene

Ethene can be polymerized to give poly(ethene). Draw two repeat units of this polymer.

$$-\!\!\left(\begin{array}{cccc} H & H & H & H \\ | & | & | & | \\ C- & C- & C- & C \\ | & | & | & | \\ H & H & H & H \end{array}\right)\!\!-$$

Other polymers

By varying the monomer, addition polymerization can produce a whole range of polymers.

For each monomer, draw two repeat units of the polymer and name the polymer.

Monomer	Polymer	Name
CH_2CHCl	$-\!\left(\begin{array}{cccc} H & H & H & H \\ C- & C- & C- & C \\ H & Cl & H & Cl \end{array}\right)\!-$	poly(vinylchloride) PVC
CH_3CHCH_2	$-\!\left(\begin{array}{cccc} H & H & H & H \\ C- & C- & C- & C \\ CH_3 & H & CH_3 & H \end{array}\right)\!-$	poly(propene)
CF_2CF_2	$-\!\left(\begin{array}{cccc} F & F & F & F \\ C- & C- & C- & C \\ F & F & F & F \end{array}\right)\!-$	poly(tetrafluororethene) PTFE

DON'T FORGET
The double bond will not be present in the polymer.

The problem with polymers

Polymer items have replaced many objects that used to be made from natural products. But disposal is a considerable problem for, unlike natural products, most polymers are not biodegradable.

What can we do with polymers once their use is over? Mention any problems associated with the methods you suggest.

Waste polymers can be recycled, although separation is a problem. They can be burnt to produce energy, but this may generate toxic gases (e.g. HCl from PVC).They can also be cracked to produce smaller, useful molecules.

Turn the page for some exam questions on this topic ➤

For more on this topic, see pages 147–148 of the *Revision Express A-level Study Guide*

Exam question 1

For each polymer shown, work out its monomer unit, then draw and name it in the monomer column. Name the polymer formed from it. Styrene has been done for you.

Monomer	Polymer	Name
propene $CH_3CH{=}CH_2$	$-\!\left(\begin{array}{c} CH_3 \\ CH-CH_2 \end{array}\right)\!-_n$	poly(propene)
ethene $CH_2{=}CH_2$	$-\!\left(CH_2-CH_2\right)\!-_n$	poly(ethene)
styrene $C_6H_5CH{=}CH_2$	$-\!\left(\begin{array}{c} C_6H_5 \\ CH-CH_2 \end{array}\right)\!-_n$	poly(styrene)
chloroethene (vinyl chloride) $CH_2{=}CHCl$	$-\!\left(\begin{array}{c} \quad Cl \\ CH_2-CH \end{array}\right)\!-_n$	poly(vinyl chloride) PVC

Exam question 2

Polymers have advantages and disadvantages. One disadvantage is that they are non-biodegradable. What is it about their structure that makes them non-biodegradable?

In order to be reactive, what would the polymer structure need?

There are no sites in the molecule that would be attractive to electrophiles or nucleophiles.

Exam question 3

Which of these compounds could undergo addition polymerization? Why could they do this?

What must the monomer unit contain?

- $CH_3CH_2CH_2CH_2CH_2CH_3$ ☐
- $CH_3CH_2CH_2CHCHCH_2CH_3$ ☑
- C_3H_6 ☑
- CHClCHCl ☑
- CH_2ClCH_3 ☐

The ticked molecules all contain a double bond, essential for addition polymerization to occur.

Alcohols

AS OCR Edexcel AQA CCEA

Alcohols contain the functional group –OH, and they have the general formula $C_nH_{2n-1}OH$

Solubility of alcohols in water

You may have noticed that ethanol and water mix.

Explain why this is the case.

What other physical property of alcohols does this explain?

This is because alcohols have H directly attached to electronegative O, so they can hydrogen bond with water. Their relatively high boiling points and low volatility can also be explained by hydrogen bonding.

SYLLABUS CHECK
Edexcel, WJEC and CCEA don't want you to know about this!

Making ethanol

The traditional method is fermentation.

What is needed for fermentation? Write an equation for the reaction of glucose during fermentation.

Using sugar, water, yeast and warmth:

$C_6H_{12}O_6 \rightarrow 2C_2H_5OH + 2CO_2$

On p. 57 you saw another method of making ethanol from ethene. What conditions are needed for this?

Industrially, ethanol can be made by reaction with steam at 300 °C, 70 atm and an H_3PO_4 catalyst.

Reactions of ethanol

Complete this chart. Fill in the structural formula and name the organic product.

Reacts with	To make	Type of reaction
$NaBr/H_2SO_4$	$C_2H_5Br + H_2O$ bromoethane	nucleophilic substitution
Na	$C_2H_5O^-Na^+ + H_2$ sodium ethoxide	reduction
O_2 and ignite	$CO_2 + H_2O$	oxidation
PCl_5	$C_2H_5Cl + HCl + POCl_3$ chloroethane	nucleophilic substitution
Ethanoic acid and H^+	$CH_3CO_2CH_3 + H_2O$ ethyl ethanoate	esterification
Ethanoyl chloride	$CH_3CO_2CH_3 + H_2O$ ethyl ethanoate	esterification
XS $Cr_2O_7^{2-}$ and H^+ under reflux	$CH_3CO_2H + H_2O$ ethanoic acid	oxidation
$Cr_2O_7^{2-}$ and H^+ distil product as it forms	$CH_3CHO + H_2O$ ethanal	mild oxidation
Conc. H_2SO_4	$C_2H_4 + H_2O$	dehydration

SYLLABUS CHECK
For WJEC you only need to know about oxidation of primary alcohols. Other boards vary a lot in their requirements. Use your syllabus to tick off the reactions you need before you start this exercise.

LINKS
This is used as a test for alcohols, as shown on pp. 73–74.

THE JARGON
Refluxing is when a solution is boiled in a flask and the vapours go up into a condenser, cool, condense and drop back into the reaction vessel to react further. XS means excess.

Turn the page for some exam questions on this topic ➤

For more on this topic, see pages 152–153 of the *Revision Express A-level Study Guide*

Exam question 1

SYLLABUS CHECK
Only OCR and CCEA require question 1.

Describe and explain how a sample of ethyl ethanoate may be prepared from ethanol and ethanoic acid in the laboratory.

What reagents are needed?

Ethanol, ethanoic acid and a catalyst of concentrated sulphuric acid are reacted.

What type of catalysis is this?

H^+ ions catalyse the reaction; these are in the same phase, so this is homogeneous catalysis. The concentrated sulphuric acid also helps to remove water from the two compounds.

What would you carry out the reaction in?

The reactants are heated in a flask at 140 °C and the ethyl ethanoate is distilled off as it forms.

How is it that the ethyl ethanoate distils off but the reactants remain in the flask?

The ethyl ethanoate has a lower boiling point than either of the reactants, so this is why it distils off.

Write a full equation for the reaction.

$$CH_3CH_2OH + CH_3CO_2H \rightleftharpoons CH_3CO_2CH_2CH_3 + H_2O$$

In order to purify the distillate, it is shaken with an aqueous solution of sodium carbonate and effervescence is seen. What is the gas likely to be and why is this done?

What reacts with a carbonate?

The gas is most likely to be carbon dioxide, and this is done to remove any traces of ethanoic acid that have distilled over with the ester.

Exam question 2

SYLLABUS CHECK
Check your syllabus to make sure which of these you need.

Fill in the missing organic product or the missing reagents and conditions.

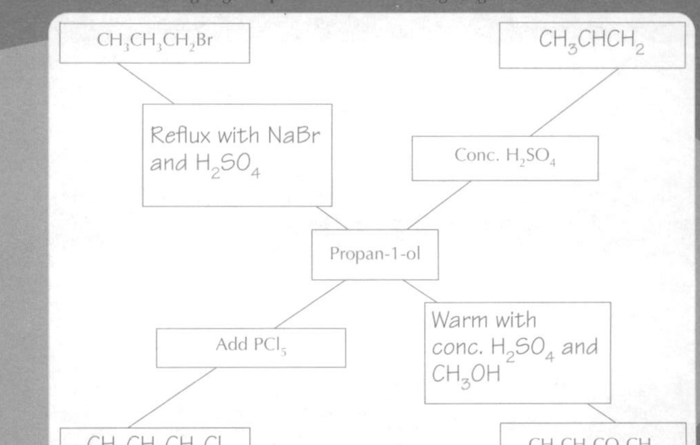

AS OCR Edexcel AQA WJEC CCEA

Classification and uses of alcohols

Here we look at the classification of alcohols into primary, secondary and tertiary, and how this affects their behaviour.

Primary, secondary or tertiary?

Label the diagrams to show which is which.

$CH_3-CH(OH)-CH_3$	$CH_3-C(OH)(CH_3)-CH_3$	CH_3-CH_2-OH
secondary	tertiary	primary

Oxidation of alcohols

Primary, secondary and tertiary alcohols behave differently during oxidation. Tick the statements that are correct here.

Mild oxidation of a primary alcohol yields a carboxylic acid	☐
Refluxing a primary alcohol with excess $H^+/Cr_2O_7^{2-}$ yields a carboxylic acid	☑
Mild oxidation of a primary alcohol yields a ketone	☐
Mild oxidation of a primary alcohol yields an aldehyde	☑
Oxidation of a secondary alcohol yields an aldehyde	☐
Oxidation of a secondary alcohol yields a ketone	☑
Oxidation of a secondary alcohol yields first a ketone then a carboxylic acid	☐
Oxidation of a tertiary alcohol stops at the formation of a ketone	☐
Oxidation of a tertiary alcohol is not possible under normal conditions	☑

LINKS
These tests can be used in the identification of alcohols, as shown on pp. 73–74.

In order to identify the class an alcohol belongs to, first it is oxidized and then the oxidation product is identified.

Using [O] to signify an oxidizing agent, write equations for the mild and complete oxidation of propan-1-ol. Name the products formed.

Mild oxidation

$CH_3CH_2CH_2OH + [O] \rightarrow CH_3CH_2CHO + H_2O$
propanal

Strong oxidation

$CH_3CH_2CHO + [O] \rightarrow CH_3CH_2CO_2H$
propanoic acid

SYLLABUS CHECK
Only WJEC and CCEA need this at AS.

Reduction of aldehydes

The aldehydes formed by oxidation of primary alcohols can themselves be reduced.

What reagent could you use?

$LiAlH_4$ or $NaBH_4$ is used as a reducing agent

Write an equation for the reduction of propanal, using [H] to signify the reducing agent.

$CH_3CH_2CHO + [H] \rightarrow CH_3CH_2CH_2OH$
propanal → propanol

Turn the page for some exam questions on this topic ➤

For more on this topic, see page 152 of the *Revision Express A-level Study Guide*

SYLLABUS CHECK
AQA only.

Exam question 1

Alcohols can undergo nucleophilic substitution reactions. Draw the structure of ethanol and indicate on your formula where it would be attractive to nucleophiles.

Draw the displayed formula for ethanol.

Nucleophiles are attracted to positive centres in the molecule. Label the bond polarity on the OH group.

$H-C(H)(H)-C(H)(H)-O^{\delta-}-H^{\delta+}$ ← attractive to nucleophiles

The presence of H^+ catalyses many reactions of alcohols. How does the presence of H^+ help the reaction?

Draw another ethanol molecule and label the bond polarity of the OH bond.

There is only one place an H^+ ion will be attracted. Use : for a lone pair and a curly arrow to show what will happen.

$H-C(H)(H)-C(H)(H)-\ddot{O}^{\delta-}-H^{\delta+} + H^+ \rightarrow H-C(H)(H)-C(H)(H)-O^+(H)-H$

What stable group could now leave the molecule?

A water molecule can now leave the molecule.

During nucleophilic substitution, one group in the molecule leaves and is replaced by another. Which is the best leaving group, H_2O or OH^-?

Since H^+ catalyses the reaction, the water molecule must be a better leaving group than $-OH$.

What type of catalysis is this?

This is an example of homogeneous catalysis, as the reactants and catalyst are in the same phase.

SYLLABUS CHECK
AQA only.

Exam question 2

The reaction of alcohols with concentrated sulphuric acid is used to make alkenes. Draw a reaction mechanism for this, using ethanol as an example. Show the part that H^+ ions play.

Draw a molecule of ethanol and mark on the bond polarity and relevant lone pairs.

Think about the role of the H^+ ion.

Draw curly arrows.

$H-C(H)(H)-C(H)(H)-\ddot{O}-H$ (protonated by H_2SO_4) $\rightarrow H-C(H)(H)-C(H)(H)-O^+(H)-H \rightarrow H_2C=CH_2$

SYLLABUS CHECK
All boards could reasonably ask this.

Exam question 3

Give uses for two named alcohols.

Ethanol is used as an alcoholic drink, a petrol substitute or a solvent.
Methanol is used as a petrol additive to improve combustion, or as a feedstock in the production of organic chemicals.

Halogenoalkanes

AS OCR Edexcel AQA WJEC CCEA

The halogenoalkanes have the general formula $C_nH_{2n+1}X$ where X is Cl, Br or I. We have seen how they can be made from alkenes and alcohols and now we see how they react.

Properties of halogenoalkanes

Draw a displayed formula for chloroethane and label the bond polarity.

```
    H   H
    |   |
H—C—C^δ+—Cl^δ−
    |   |
    H   H
```

Can it hydrogen bond with water? Check to see if it has H directly bonded to N, O, F. Does it have a permanent dipole?

With no H atom bonded directly to N, O or F, there is no possibility of hydrogen bonding but it does have a permanent dipole.

Look at the data below and compare the boiling temperature of chloroethane with the boiling temperatures of propan-1-ol and butane.

Name	T_B (°C)	M_r
propan-1-ol	97.5	60.1
chloroethane	12.5	64.5
butane	−0.4	58.1

Chloroethane, propan-1-ol and butane have similar mass and similar strength of van der Waals forces. The boiling temperature is lower for chloroethane than for propan-1-ol, which can hydrogen bond, but higher than for butane, which has no permanent dipole.

Would you expect chloroethane to be miscible with water?

Since it cannot hydrogen bond, chloroethane is not miscible with water.

THE JARGON
Miscible means that it will mix.

Substitution reactions of halogenoalkanes

Look again at your diagram of chloroethane then read through these statements and tick any row that has a correct observation and deduction.

Observation	Deduction	
The carbon adjacent to Cl has a partial positive charge	It will be attractive to electrophiles	
The carbon adjacent to Cl has a partial positive charge	It will be attractive to nucleophiles.	✓
If sodium hydroxide is reacted with it, the OH⁻ ion can act as an electron donor	It is an electrophile	
If sodium hydroxide is reacted with it, the OH⁻ ion can act as an electron donor	It is a nucleophile	✓

SYLLABUS CHECK
Check your syllabus now to see which reactions it mentions. There is much variation between syllabuses.

When halogenoalkanes are heated under reflux with aqueous NaOH, a substitution reaction occurs. The halogenoalkane is hydrolysed.

Write an equation to show the reaction of chloroethane and aqueous NaOH.

$$CH_3CH_2Cl_{(l)} + OH^-_{(aq)} \rightarrow CH_3CH_2OH_{(aq)} + Cl^-_{(aq)}$$

When refluxed with ethanolic NaOH, an elimination reaction occurs.

Write an equation for the reaction.

$$CH_3CH_2Cl_{(l)} + OH^-_{(eth)} \rightarrow CH_2{=}CH_{2(g)} + H_2O_{(l)} + Cl^-_{(eth)}$$

Another nucleophilic substitution occurs when chloroethane reacts with concentrated ammonia in ethanol.

How can ammonia act as a nucleophile and what will be the product of this reaction?

The nitrogen has a lone pair and so it reacts with chloroethane to form an amine.

Turn the page for some exam questions on this topic ➤

For more on this topic, see page 150 of the *Revision Express A-level Study Guide*

Exam question 1

SYLLABUS CHECK
This question is for everyone.

5.00 cm³ of 1-iodobutane were refluxed with an excess of NaOH and 2.10 g of the product butan-1-ol were collected. What was the percentage yield of this reaction? (M_r iodobutane = 184.0, M_r butanol = 74.1, density iodobutane = 1.62 g cm⁻³)

$CH_3CH_2CH_2CH_2I + OH^- \rightarrow CH_3CH_2CH_2CH_2OH + I^-$

density = mass / volume

Calculate the mass of iodobutane used.

mass = density × volume
= 1.62 × 5.00
= 8.10 g

Calculate moles of iodobutane.

$n = m / M_r$ = 8.10/184.0
= 0.0440 mol

How many moles of product will it give?

1 mol iodobutane → 1 mol butanol
so we will get 0.0440 mol butanol

Calculate the maximum yield of butanol.

$m = nM_r$ = (0.0440 × 74.1) = 3.26 g
so maximum yield is 3.26 g butanol

% yield = (obtained yield)/(possible yield) × 100%
= (2.10/3.26) × 100%
= 64.4%

Exam question 2

SYLLABUS CHECK
This question is for AQA and Edexcel only. Edexcel does not require you to know how to convert a nitrile to a carboxylic acid.

The reaction of bromoethane with cyanide ions can be used to extend the length of the carbon chain in a molecule. Describe how this reaction should be carried out and show how the product is converted to a carboxylic acid.

THE JARGON
A nitrile has the functional group —C≡N.

State the reaction conditions and the product.

Reflux with potassium cyanide in ethanol.
It makes a nitrile.

Write an equation for the reaction of bromoethane with CN⁻ ions.

$$CH_3CH_2Br + KCN \rightarrow CH_3CH_2C{\equiv}N + KBr$$

Explain how is the nitrile converted to a carboxylic acid.

Refluxing with dilute sulphuric acid converts the nitrile to a carboxylic acid.

Write an equation for the reaction of propanenitrile with dilute sulphuric acid.

$$CH_3CH_2C{\equiv}N + 2H_2O \rightarrow CH_3CH_2CO_2H + NH_3$$

You might finally want to convert this to propanol. What type of reagent would you use to convert a carboxylic acid to an alcohol?

I would use a reducing agent.

AS OCR Edexcel AQA CCEA

Reaction mechanisms of halogenoalkanes

We look at the nucleophilic substitution of halogenoalkanes and how it relates to rate of hydrolysis. We also look at elimination.

SYLLABUS CHECK
Edexcel does not require *any* mechanisms, so go straight to exam question 2 on page 70.

SYLLABUS CHECK
AQA, OCR and CCEA only.

Nucleophilic substitution of primary halogenoalkanes

This substitution is a one-step reaction that occurs in aqueous conditions. Follow the steps to show how it works.

Draw a diagram of bromoethane and label the partial charges. Draw the attacking OH^- ion with its lone pair.

Draw two curly arrows to show the one-step substitution. Show the products.

$H_3C{-}CH_2^{\delta+}{-}Br^{\delta-} + OH^- \rightarrow H_3C{-}CH_2{-}OH + Br^-$

Elimination of hydrogen bromide from bromoethane

SYLLABUS CHECK
AQA and OCR only.

If the reaction between bromoethane and NaOH is carried out in anhydrous conditions in ethanolic solution, there is a very different result.

What product will form? How is the OH^- ion acting here?

Ethene forms. In an elimination reaction the OH^- ions act as a base by accepting protons.

Add curly arrows to show how bromoethane reacts with OH^- to release a molecule of water and a Br^- ion. Draw the products.

$H{-}CH_2{-}CH_2{-}Br + OH^- \rightarrow H_2C{=}CH_2 + Br^- + H_2O$

THE JARGON
A tertiary halogenoalkane is where there are three methyl groups attached to the carbon atom adjacent to the halogen.

Elimination is more likely than substitution in tertiary halogenoalkanes.

Draw the simplest possible tertiary bromoalkane and name it.

$CH_3{-}C(Br)(CH_3){-}CH_3$ 2-bromomethylpropane is the simplest tertiary bromoalkane

SYLLABUS CHECK
AQA only.

Tick the reasons why you think tertiary halogenoalkanes are more likely to undergo elimination than primary halogenoalkanes.

Alkyl groups push electrons onto the carbon adjacent to the halogen	✓
Alkyl groups make the partial charge on the carbon more positive	
Alkyl groups make the partial charge on the carbon less positive	✓
The alkyl groups are bulky and get in the way of the attacking OH^- nucleophile	✓
The OH^- can only get near the outer hydrogens, so it acts as a base and pulls a hydrogen off	✓
The effect of alkyl groups is to make the carbon attached to the halogen less attractive to nucleophiles	✓

Turn the page for some exam questions on this topic ➤

For more on this topic, see page 145 of the *Revision Express A-level Study Guide*

Exam question 1

SYLLABUS CHECK
OCR and CCEA only.

Explain how and why the rate of hydrolysis of halogenoalkanes varies with the particular halogen present and explain how you could demonstrate this.

How does the rate of hydrolysis vary? Add a label to the arrow on this diagram.

$-C-Cl \quad -C-Br \quad -C-I$ → increased rate of reaction

Why does the halogen make a difference?

The easier it is for the halogen bond to break, the easier it will be for the one-step reaction to occur. Going down group 7, C–X bond length increases, hence the bond strength decreases, making it easier for the C–X bond to break. This makes hydrolysis easier as you descend the group.

How would you demonstrate this? Number this sequence of steps to show how.

Add 2 cm^3 of ethanol to act as a solvent	2
Warm the tubes in a water bath to 50 °C	3
Precipitates of silver halides will form	6
Place 2 cm^3 of silver nitrate solution in each of three tubes	1
When up to 50 °C, add 0.5 cm^3 of 1-chlorobutane to tube A, 0.5 cm^3 of 1-bromobutane to tube B and 0.5 cm^3 of 1-iodobutane to tube C	4
Precipitation will occur most rapidly in tube C, then tube B and finally tube A	7
Replace in the water bath and observe	5

Exam question 2

SYLLABUS CHECK
All boards.

When 2-bromo-3-methylbutane reacts with NaOH under various conditions, a variety of products are possible. Complete this chart to show the possibilities. Draw formulae for the products.

Could more than one product form if OH^- acts as a base?

OH^- acts as	Reaction type	Product
Base	elimination	$H_2C{=}CH{-}CH(CH_3){-}CH_3$
Base	elimination	$(CH_3)HC{=}C(CH_3)_2$
Nucleophile	nucleophilic substitution	$CH_3{-}CH(OH){-}CH(CH_3){-}CH_3$

Uses of halogenoalkanes

Fluorohalogenoalkanes and fluoroalkanes have many uses but there are pitfalls too.

Chlorofluorocarbons (CFCs)

Draw a displayed formula for 1,1,1-trichloroethane.

```
    Cl  H
    |   |
Cl—C———C—H
    |   |
    Cl  H
```

1,1,1-trichloroethane

This substance was once used as the thinner for Tippex and other liquid paper products. Why is its use a problem?

CFCs like this can enter the upper atmosphere, where they are responsible for ozone depletion.

How is it that such compounds can reach the upper atmosphere without reacting with anything on the way?

The strong C–Cl bonds do not readily break, so it does not react in the lower atmosphere.

How do the C–Cl bonds break when they reach the upper atmosphere?

In the upper atmosphere the C–Cl bond absorbs high-energy ultraviolet radiation.

What happens to the bond there, and why is this a problem?

Homolytic fission produces free radicals, which cause ozone depletion.

Uses of CFCs

Say whether the following statements are true of false; explain what is wrong with the statements that are false.

If your fridge contains CFCs then care should be taken when disposing of it	True
CFCs have been used as the blowing agent in making polystyrene foams	True
Chloroethane can be used to make the polymer PVC	False it's chloro**ethene**
Halogenoalkanes make very useful intermediates in organic synthesis because the halogen can be readily replaced by nucleophilic addition	False it's nucleophilic substitution
Tetrafluoroethene is used to make the polymer PTFE	True
Even if we stopped using CFCs immediately, it would be a long time before ozone depletion abated because the free radicals they produce are not used up during reactions	True one Cl· is able to catalyse many reactions
CFCs replaced butane as a propellant in aerosols; now butane has come back into use despite its obvious hazards	True
CFCs are used in degreasing and dry-cleaning; covalent bonding makes them good solvents for organic compounds	True

Turn the page for some exam questions on this topic ➤

Exam question 1

Chlorofluorocarbons (CFCs) are now known to cause depletion of the ozone layer that protects us from harmful UV radiation. Using CCl_2F_2 as an example, outline this process, explaining the way in which the action is catalytic.

To help you this time, the steps have been given in the right order but the right-hand column is for you to write the equations. Use the text to help you.

THE JARGON
Free radicals have an unpaired electron, which makes them very reactive. The chlorine free radical may be written as Cl· or just Cl.

DON'T FORGET
You get this by adding together the equations for the second and third steps in the process.

CFCs drift up to the upper atmosphere where they absorb energy, breaking the C–Cl bond in the molecule and forming Cl· radicals	Step 1 $CCl_2F_{2(g)} \rightarrow CF_2Cl\cdot_{(g)} + Cl\cdot_{(g)}$
The chlorine free radicals react with ozone and form ClO· radicals	Step 2 $Cl\cdot_{(g)} + O_{3(g)} \rightarrow ClO\cdot_{(g)} + O_{2(g)}$
The ClO· radical reacts with oxygen radicals present in the upper atmosphere, making oxygen gas and restoring Cl· free radicals	Step 3 $ClO\cdot_{(g)} + O\cdot_{(g)} \rightarrow O_{2(g)} + Cl\cdot_{(g)}$
The overall reaction is removal of ozone	$O_{3(g)} + O\cdot_{(g)} \rightarrow 2O_{2(g)}$

Exam question 2

Analysis of a halogenoalkane shows it to contain 17.8% C, 52.6% Cl, 1.5% H and 28.1% F. Calculate its empirical formula, and given that it has $M_r = 135$, obtain its molecular formula. Draw its four isomers. Use C = 12, Cl = 35.5, F = 19, H = 1.

	C	Cl	H	F
How many grams of each element would there be in 100 g?	17.8	52.6	1.5	28.1
How many moles of each?	1.48	1.48	1.5	1.48
What is the simplest ratio?	1	1	1	1

What is the empirical formula?

One unit of CHClF has a relative mass of 67.5, so there must be two units of CHClF in the molecular formula, which is $C_2H_2Cl_2F_2$.

```
   Cl  F
   |   |
H—C———C—H
   |   |
   Cl  F
```

1,1-dichloro-2,2-difluoroethane

```
   Cl  Cl
   |   |
F—C———C—H
   |   |
   F   H
```

1,2dichloro-1,1-difluoroethane

```
   Cl  Cl
   |   |
H—C———C—H
   |   |
   F   F
```

1,2-dichloro-1,2-difluoroethane

```
   Cl  F
   |   |
F—C———C—H
   |   |
   Cl  H
```

1,1-dichloro-1,2-difluoroethane

AS OCR Edexcel AQA WJEC CCEA

Organic analysis

You will meet these tests in your practical work but they also appear in theory papers.

What are the tests?

For each of the tests and observations here, say what functional group is present

Test	Observation	Functional group present
Add bromine water and shake	Bromine decolorizes	alkene
Addition of H^+/MnO_4^-	Purple colour decolorized	alkene
Add PCl_5	Steamy fumes (of HCl)	alcohol
Warm with acidified $Cr_2O_7^{2-}$	Solution turns from orange to brown to green	alcohols: primary and secondary
Add Tollen's reagent and warm	A silver layer is deposited on the sides of the tube	aldehyde
Add Fehling's solution and warm	Brick red precipitate	aldehyde
Hydrolysis by base followed by addition of $HNO_3/AgNO_3$	Formation of white, cream or yellow precipitate	halogenoalkane
Add sodium carbonate solution	Effervescence (CO_2 forms)	carboxylic acid

THE JARGON
Tollen's reagent is silver nitrate dissolved in ammonia solution. Fehling's is an alkaline solution of Cu^{2+} ions.

Using infrared spectroscopy

Label the O–H peak and the C–O peak.

Spectrum of ethanol

IR (liquid film)
O–H
C–O
3500 3000 2500 2000 1800 1600 1400 1200 1000 800 600
Wavenumber (cm^{-1})

SYLLABUS CHECK
OCR requires you to interpret infrared spectroscopy data, but you do not need to how the technique works.

Label the C=O peak. Remember that butan-2-one is a ketone.

Spectrum of butan-2-one

IR (liquid film)
C=O
3500 3000 2500 2000 1800 1600 1400 1200 1000 800 600
Wavenumber (cm^{-1})

DON'T FORGET

	Wavenumber (cm^{-1})
C–O in alcohols	1000–300
C=O in ketones and carboxylic acids	1680–750
O–H in alcohols	3230–3550
O–H in carboxylic acids	2500–3300 broad

Turn the page for some exam questions on this topic ➤

For more on this topic, see pages 160–161 of the *Revision Express A-level Study Guide*

Exam question 1

LINKS
Check p. 52 to remind yourself what is meant by structural isomerism and *cis/trans* isomerism.

A, which has $M_r = 74$, is tested with PCl_5 and found to release steamy fumes of B. When A is treated with concentrated sulphuric acid, it produces two different structural isomers, C and D. When A is oxidized using $H^+/Cr_2O_7^{2-}$ the colour of the solution turns from orange to green but the product formed, E, does not give a positive test with Tollen's reagent. Name each of A to E and write balanced equations for all reactions.

From the PCl_5 test and M_r, what can you say about A? What is B?

A is an alcohol; M_r suggests C_4H_9OH, butanol. B is HCl gas.

Write an equation for this reaction.

The equation for the reaction of A with PCl_5 is

$$C_4H_9OH + PCl_5 \rightarrow C_4H_9Cl + HCl + POCl_3$$

Write an equation for the dehydration of A. Draw the displayed formulae and name the two structural isomers, C and D, that form.

Dehydration of A is given by

$$C_4H_9OH \rightarrow C_4H_8 + H_2O$$

This gives two possible isomers, C and D.

$H_2C{=}CH{-}CH_2{-}CH_3$ (displayed formula) — but-1-ene

$CH_3{-}CH{=}CH{-}CH_3$ (displayed formula) — but-2-ene

Could A be butan-1-ol? If not, what is it?

Butan-1-ol would only give one dehydration product, so A must be butan-2-ol.

On oxidation does an aldehyde form? If not, what has?

On oxidation the negative reaction with Tollen's means an aldehyde does not form; it is a ketone.

Write an equation for this oxidation and name the product.

$C_4H_9OH + [O] \rightarrow C_4H_8O + H_2O$. E is butan-2-one.

SYLLABUS CHECK
Question 2(a) for OCR only.

Exam question 2

Label any significant peaks in this spectrum and use them to identify the functional groups present.

You only need to think about whether it has O–H, C=O or C–O. Assume no other functional groups are present.

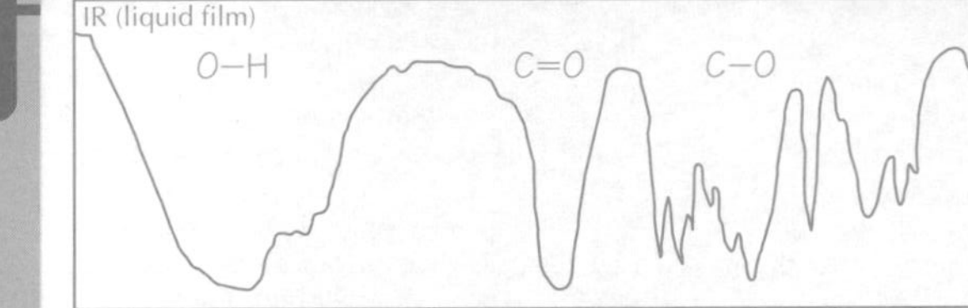

There is a broad O–H peak at around 3000 cm^{-1}, a C=O peak at 1700 cm^{-1} and a C–O peak at about 1200 cm^{-1}. So it must be a carboxylic acid.

SYLLABUS CHECK
The rest of the question is for any board.

Index

*Note: The page numbers in the index refer to the question section of the book. However, you may need to check the relevant answer pages for full information on a topic.